TAKING THE PISS OUT OF CANCER

ORLA
KELLY
PUBLISHING

Raymond Poole

Published by Orla Kelly Publishing.

For further information on national & international distribution, contact OrlaKellyPublishing.com, Orla@OrlaKellyPublishing.com

All profits from the sale of this book go to support the Marie Keating Foundation.

First Edition 2020

ISBN 978-1-912328-78-9

Orla Kelly Publishing
27 Kilbrody
Mount oval
Rochestown
Cork
Ireland

Dedication

This book is dedicated to my father who had many a battle with cancer.

Dad, you are loved more than you will ever know. Your shadow has cast an impression that will live long after the sun has set.

Acknowledgements

I want to thank the magnificent folks at *The Marie Keating Foundation* who tirelessly strive to make this world a better place for those living with and through cancer. Our journeys are lighter because of your hard work and words are inadequate to show our appreciation.

To Karl Smyth, for providing the artwork for this book on a pro bono basis but more importantly his friendship over the past number of years.

To Edwin Sammon, a huge heartfelt thank you for reading a draft of the book and supplying the foreword. I can say, without any chance of being contradicted, that I empathise with you for now having two voices in your head – sorry about that!

To Geoff, Angelina, Breda and Lorraine, your infectious laughter, good humour and resilience to stay with me through the bad times as much as the good times, only goes to show the strength of our bond.

To Peter McVeigh, because if I don't mention him in this book, he will stop providing me with his pre-release songs and that just wouldn't do! But more importantly because his music and friendship has been a constant in my life throughout my journey with cancer. Thanks fella!

To Bill Kelly, a man who came into my life because of prostate cancer and someone who has provided me the space to be vulnerable, strong but most importantly, the space for laughter and true friendship. You are a beacon of hope in what so easily could become a dark place. Thank you!

To Lorraine O'Reilly and Simon Daly for reviewing the book and providing feedback to help make it a book worth reading.

Thanks to Jean O'Sullivan of Red Pen Edits for putting manners on my punctuation, sentence formation and even finding her inner Dublin accent. To Orla Kelly Publishing for bringing it all together and turning the voices in my head into this magnificent book.

To Denise Breen for reminding me that prostate cancer also affects those women who are transgender or intersex. We must never forget if we were born with a penis it came with a prostate; so ladies, please stay diligent and get your PSA blood tests done annually.

Finally, to Stephen Bradley, you signed a copy of your book for me with the inscription 'Twitter Brothers'! Hopefully, one day when this pandemic ends, we will become 'Coffee Brothers'! Stay safe, take care of yourself and look after Jackie O.

Soundtrack To Book

Similar to my previous book (*Nothing's So Bad That It Couldn't Be Worse*), I have created a Spotify playlist to accompany this book. For some it may add that extra dimension but what I hope it adds is some space to just close your eyes, lie back and listen to music. Let the notes sooth your pain and the lyrics ease your torment. Know that on your journey with cancer there is help, assistance and those that are willing to reach out with a hand of help. Never be too proud to grab for that hand or too stubborn to think you can take this journey alone. Cancer can bring people into your life you otherwise may never have met and by allowing those people in, they will light that dark path like fireflies on a hot summer night. Don't be alone taking this journey, we are here for one another.

Safe travels my friends.

May you find hope, light and comfort in places you least expect to.

When you are ready, just go to my website www.raymondpoole.com to locate the link to the Spotify playlist.

Contents

———— ⚜ ————

Introduction

How does one introduce this book and indeed, prepare the reader for what they are about to encounter? This is something I have wrestled with for a long time. It is not a book like any I have read, and I have no doubt it will not be for everyone. My best description would be to imagine Ricky Gervais and Roddy Doyle having a conversation about prostate cancer and you will be somewhat close to it.

It is a raw account of my journey with prostate cancer from diagnosis through to surgery, post-surgery and beyond, through dialogue between two voices in my head. It has not been written to deliberately offend anyone but may do so. The purpose of the book is to be raw, in-your-face, and explain in no uncertain detail what that journey can be like for some.

When I was diagnosed with prostate cancer, more than anything, I wanted to hear a survivor's story but with no restrictions. I wanted to know how they felt, what they thought and how it was impacting upon them both physically and emotionally. To that end, I wrote my own thoughts down as they happened in this dialogue format sounding like two inner city Dubs.

It is written with dark humour scattered throughout. I guess if you are someone who would be offended by dark humour, then don't read it – this book is definitely not for you!

As you encounter each chapter, it will be dated with the day I wrote it. In doing it this way, you can track my journey more accurately and see how my body healed and my mind lagged behind.

For those who do read it, I hope you enjoy the read. That is, if one can enjoy a read about cancer. If cancer has taught me one thing, it's that it hates the sound of uncontrollable laughter. So laugh out loud, laugh quietly to yourself but most of all, just laugh.

Safe travel cancer warriors' and carers xx

Foreword by Edwin Sammon

-Well, this should be easy, writing four words.

-What are you talking about? It's not 'four words', it's 'foreword'. F – O – R – E, as in, before.

-Is this a book about golf? Because I don't know much about golf.

-It's not about golf.

-I know it's the sport of kings but that's all I really know.

-No, it's not about... and also, that's not correct. You're thinking of horseracing. Look, maybe you should let me do the talking.

-But it's a book!

-Look, don't get smart with me, I'm technically the same person as you.

-Whaddaya mean?

-Well, yer man Raymond, who wrote the book, he uses the same framing device – a conversation he's having in his head between two fictional characters as a means of dealing with trauma.

-Oh, is that how people deal with trauma?

-Well, everybody is different. If you're a comedian...

-Which Ed is...

-Which we are...

-Oh, that's a bit confusing.

-It's not confusing, it's meta. We're Ed and he's us. The foreword is written in the same style as the book. So, it's clever.

-I don't think it's as clever as you think it is.

-Look, we've got to keep this short and sweet – talk about how Ed connected with the book and how a lot of it resonated with his own cancer experience.

-Yeah, but he had it in the bowel.

-Yeah, and there are parts of this book that make him glad he only got it there. Prostate cancer is no joke.

-But you have to find the humour in it!

-Oh, absolutely. And having bowel cancer made it easier. It's the part of the body that's already an established comedy area – you're already set up for laughs.

-Because if you didn't laugh, you would only end up crying.

-Crying is alright though. I mean, that's what Raymond is talking about in the book, letting all your emotions out.

-He talks about a lot of things that Ed can recognise.

-Like being taken by surprise with your emotions when you're going through something like this. Anything can set them off. An advert can make you weep when the actors playing father and son bond over a great deal on car insurance.

-And then you end up laughing because it's silly that an advert made you cry.

-And let's not forget the music.

-Oh, yeah, Ed loves his music. That deffo helped him through it. Just putting on his favourite albums and getting lost in the tunes. That helped the time go by and cleared his head.

-It's an important lesson featured in the book.

-It is. And not just for someone affected by cancer, for everyone. Doing something to take your mind off things helps. It's like a meditation kind of thing.

-Without the actual meditation.

-Well, it can be. But it can also be knitting or making a *papier-mâché* Viking helmet or watching a goldfish swimming around for an hour. Whatever floats your boat.

-It can be floating a boat?

-Sure, and then putting it inside a bottle – whatever activity you choose you lose yourself in.

-This book is something you can get lost in.

-Oh, nice.

-Did you like that?

-Yes, bringing it full circle. It's a funny, honest read that brought a lot of old memories back, as well as the old emotions. And emotionally, you have to take care of yourself when you're being physically challenged by cancer.

- Yes, all your emotions are heightened, you find yourself living moment to moment and as a result, you do appreciate every one of them.

-You appreciate them more. The moments.

-Yes, exactly. The good and the bad. They are all ingredients in the soup of life.

-And they are deffo some of the same ingredients in both their soups.

-Like what?

-Similar croutons in a different flavoured soup.

-I don't think it's really the best comparison. You could say it makes you appreciate soup more.

-Oh yeah? Sure, who can't relate to soup?

-No one. That's who.

Taking the Pi55 Out of Cancer

Timeline

To orientate yourself through the book, here are the key dates:

- July 2016 PSA blood test reading 9.0

- August 2016 PSA blood test reading 10.0

- 5 December 2016 First prostate biopsies are all clear

- 8 December 2016 Diagnosed with sepsis following biopsy, hospitalised for 11 days

- January 2017 PSA blood test reading 19.8

- February 2017 Infection in hip

- March 2017 Lung infection

- July 2017 Bowel infection, hospitalised for 7 days

- 11 August 2017 Confirmed prostate cancer

- 9 October 2017 Radical prostatectomy with robotic surgery (first male C-section)

- 25 November 2019 Life is precious

- 06 July 2020 Second male C-section

- 28 August 2020 I'm still standing (and dancing!)

CHAPTER 1

Numbness

17 February 2018

-Wha the fuck? February 2018? Sure wha about the next dialogue written in 2017, does he understand the months of the year?

-Yeah, he noticed he never wrote anything about how they felt when he was diagnosed.

-But tha means everyone who now reads this hasn't a feck about who we are as they're reading this first.

-Well, they can jump to August 2017 if they like or just hold on and enjoy the ride for now.

-Beginning to think he's losing the run of himself and he thinks he's George Lucas or some head like tha, screwing around with the sequence of his dialogues.

-If he thought he was George Lucas he would have put this dialogue at the end of the book.

-Jaysus, ye're right there! Fair play to ya. So, do ya think he can remember how he felt back then? After all, it was August 2017 he was diagnosed.

-He hasn't got feckin dementia – it was prostate cancer he had. Tha doesn't affect yer memory.

-Ya sure 'bout tha?

-No, but think he will recall, not likely to EVER forget.

-Well, go on then, which one of us is goin to start tha jackanory then?

-I can, if ya want. Come here though, if he is publishing this as a book and it goes global, do ya think everyone round tha globe will understand our slang?

-No idea, but sure they say the Irish are everywhere, so if that's the case, then no worries there.

-Yeah, guess so.

-Be interesting to know though where it's read and wha they think.

 -Is tha yer way of looking for fan mail?

-Fan mail? For fuck sake! Wha century where ya born in? It's email nowadays, ya tool!

-Ok, ye're doin me head in. Just let's get goin, where do we start this one from then?

-I guess at the beginning. Sure isn't tha wha the guy up North suggested?

-Who ya talkin bout? He doesn't know tha many folks North of the Liffey.

-No, ya eejit! I'm talkin 'bout the guy up in Belfast. The one tha writes those songs and plays a wee bit on the guitar. Ya know who I mean – wha's the 'situation man'. Ya know him!

-Ah Jaysus, tha fella! Here, ya know he said they really don't say the SITCH-E-AYSHUN up there?

-I do, but sure tha's just because he's a catholic-atheist. Now, if he was a protestant-atheist he would know all 'bout the situation.

-Ah, good for ya.

-We may just have lost half our readership slagging off the atheists and Catholics all in one go.

-Ah sure, if they get upset over tha, then they best not read the rest of this.

-So, the beginning?

-Right, how far back we goin again? Will we go back to his first biopsy on 5 December 2016 and the claret wine or jump to 11 August 2017 and the diagnosis?

-Ah sure, start from the very beginning.

-Grand so. Well, he went for his first biopsy on 5 December 2016, had 'bout 25+ samples taken...

-Here, before ya go on.

-Jaysus, I haven't even started yet and ye're interrupting me!

-I know but best tell folks wha is 'bout to happen is 1-in-100 chance of happening, so don't scare the shit out of them. Bad enough they'll be pissin themselves.

-Anyways, as I was sayin, he got the biopsy and after it, he was peeing claret for 'bout three days.

-Claret, now explain tha one.

-His urine was dark red and should have been more of a rosé, if ya get my drift?

-So, wha ya are tryin to depict?

-Jaysus, go on will ya with ya fancy words – depict!

-As I was sayin, after a prostate biopsy it's normal to pass blood in yer urine, but it should be light red in colour.

-Yeah, that's wha I said! Look this is goin to be a very long feckin dialogue to start with if ya keep on interrupting me.

-Go on with ya so.

-Ok, he bled – tha is, he pissed blood like dark claret red wine for three days and went to A&E. He'd basically got sepsis.

-But not everyone gets sepsis?

-We already said tha. Listen, let me tell the story or I will just feck off.

-Ok, go on.

-Anyways, he had four infections over the next number of months and in July 2017 he went in for more scans etc. He was officially diagnosed with prostate cancer on 11 August 2017.

-He will never forget tha date.

-Indeedo, and when he was told it felt surreal. Almost like he was walking in a dreamlike state. He could hear noises around him and see people, but it was like an out of body experience.

-And the Missus?

-Yeah, she felt like they had been run over by a steamroller.

-It went on for weeks after, the sensation, as they came to grips with the news.

-Sure thing. Sure, no one wants to hear they have The Big C.

-Cancer. Fuckin even now when I say the word, I get shivers through me body.

-Ya don't have a body, ya twat!

-Ah, shut up! They don't know tha yet as they haven't read the other dialogue in the next chapter.

-Yeah, forgot tha. Go on then.

-Anyways, here he is in mid-February 2018 and he still feels somewhat numb to the whole event after havin the surgery on 9 October 2017.

-But good news is, he is still alive.

-Talk about statin the obvious. Sure if he wasn't, he wouldn't be writin this, now would he?

-Well, it could be someone else is writin it if he died.

-Hardly. How would they hear us, ya gobshite? So, as I was sayin before I was rudely interrupted, even to this day he still feels somewhat numb 'bout the whole thing.

-Like comfortably numb – now tha's a great title for a song.

-Are ya on drugs or wha? It already is a song by Pink Floyd.

-Ah! Ya know he loves his music.

-Jaysus, I really think after all this time, ya are deffo losing it.

-Well, who wouldn't, having only yous to talk with.

-Ah, go fuck yerself!

-Jaysus, wish I could. Bet he even wishes he could.

-STOP! They haven't read about tha yet.

-Aren't they in for some surprises then...

-Do ya think we have their attention now and they'll read some more?

-Well, if they don't, they'll never know wha they have missed.

Do you remember the nights we'd lay awake?

There was never ever nothing we could take,

to calm our thoughts or control our fears,

my dear.

-Do ya know who tha is?

-How could I not? He says tha guy's music kept him sane throughout this entire journey. Its Peter McVeigh's tune *Stronger.*

-Go on with ya then, dare ya sing the rest.

-Ya do know this is a book and they can't hear anything?

-Ah, tha's where ye're wrong. They can listen to it on the Spotify playlist he made to accompany his other book. Tha's of course if they haven't already heard Peter McVeigh sing it.

-Don't mention the war!

-Wha war?

-The fact he released another book before this one. He promised us this would be his first publication. Fuckin turncoat!

-Well, he is dyslexic, so it'd take him to publish his first book second and his second book first. Now, will ya let it go and just move on.

-Sheer con-fuck-usion.

-Without a doubt.

-We finished now?

-Think so. Ya off then?

-Yeah, goin to listen to some more music now.

-Yeah, think I'll join ya. It's a day for music.

-Feck, every day is a day for music!

-If anyone was offended by any of our comments, etc. Guess wha? We don't give a fuck! Ha ha ha! Only jokin! Read the rest of the book. It's worth the effort. ENJOY!!

-Til next time then.

-Til then...

CHAPTER 2

Memes

13 August 2017

-Jaysus! So, wha's this all about?

-Prostate cancer!

-Fuck tha! Why are we doing it?

-We're the voices in yer man's head.

-Do we have names?

-Nah, tha's too airy fairy, just voices.

-Ya mean like Roddy Doyle's posts?

-Yeah, tha's it.

-Won't he be fuckin fuming? Doyler like, will we be sued for artistic cogging?

-Jaysus, never thought of tha.

-Claim ignorance if we are, sure we be good at tha.

-What's the setting? Ya know, like Doyler is two auld geezers sittin in a pub over a pint?

-Well, this guy doesn't drink.

-Ah, for fuck sake! How did we end up with this gig!? What about in a café?

-Nah, doesn't drink coffee or tea either.

-Then, where the feck are we?

-Well, he goes for walks with his mate Enda to Punchestown and Glendalough, so we could be there.

-Right, is he gay so? Cause I'm not playing a feckin gay. The lads down the pub will only take the piss out of me.

-No, he's not gay.

-Ok then.

-We just have to be frank and honest.

-Ah Jaysus! Ya said we were not going to have names. I know he spent two years in South Africa but I am not taking a feckin name like Frank or Honest, screw tha! They can keep all those feckin Precious and Beauty names over there. We're Irish!

-No, ya eejit! We just have to be truthful about what he talks about. Ya know, not to hide it, put it out there – like telling it as it happens.

-Phew, tha's a relief because this gig was looking a bit too politically correct and up yer own hole type of thing for me.

-Well, there will be plenty of tha!

-Plenty wha?

-Up yer hole – it's prostate cancer, after all.

-Ye're so fuckin smart, aren't ya?

-So, how do we start?

-With the diagnosis.

-Ok, so how did he get it? Smoking fags, drinking the sweet creamy black stuff or perhaps smoking a little weed, snorting the talc and shooting up?

-Nah, never smoked, drank alcohol, took drugs.

-Jaysus! Are ya sure this guy is Irish? So was he one of those tree-hugging clog-wearing vegan types who didn't get the right protein?

-Nah, a good auld Irish male. Spuds, two veg and meat man.

-Tha's it – the fuckin spuds! Sure, didn't they kill half us off in the 1840s during the famine.

-For fuck sake! It was the lack of spuds tha killed us, not eatin too many.

-How auld is the poor fucker? Sixty-five, seventy, eighty – wha?

-Fifty-four!

-Jaysus! A baby in the world of prostate issues.

-He's dyslexic, ya know.

-Is tha how he got it then?

-No, it's not, but he doesn't always say things the right way round or spell them right.

-Well, tha's not going to be a feckin issue here, now is it?

-So, wha's the prognosis?

-Well, he got a prostate biopsy done, three of the five samples were cancerous.

-Fuck. Tha's a lot!

-Not really. He had an MRI beforehand so they knew exactly where to look.

-Did it hurt? I mean, the tube up the arse?

-He said it didn't, just uncomfortable and in yer head, sorta.

-So, what happens during it?

-They examine ya first by putting a finger up there and feeling the prostate.

-Ouch! Hope the fucker putting the finger up had small fingers!

-Then they place a small scope up yer arse, look around and then have a very thin needle tha can take samples, all over in five to ten minutes.

-Brave fuckin man, letting the doc shove tha up him!

-Best bit is ye're not asleep and simply walk in and out of the room with no sickness or anything.

-Do ya go home straight after?

-Nah, ya hang around til ya have a piss.

-Well, tha shouldn't be too long if ya have prostate issues.

-Actually, it can take a bit of time and ye're asked to drink a jug of water. He was waiting over an hour to pee. In his case, he passed clots of blood which hurt a little but once the water started flowing, all was good.

-Ah Jaysus! I'm a little squeamish. Did ya have to be so feckin graphic?

-Well, no point writing this book if we don't tell it as it is.

-I suppose but was he in pain?

-No, more uncomfortable than pain and a little embarrassing for some men. As if the whole experience wasn't bad enough, he was also abused as a child, so ya can imagine this caused a few more mental issues than most. But he deals with tha in his other book, so enough said 'bout tha here.

-Fuck. Is tha how he got it? Been abused like, did it do something to his water works tha caused the cancer?

-No, nothing to do with it.

-Jaysus, tha's a relief. So, then wha?

-Well, ya can pass blood for a few days after in yer piss and when ya do a dump.

-Ah Jaysus!

-Plus, there could be blood in yer semen for up to three or four weeks after.

-D'ya mean ya can still have sex even with prostate cancer?

-Yeah, but tha's if ya can get it up. Some guys end up, ya know, not able perform too well... bit of a limp asparagus.

-Poor fuck.

-Well, tha's it for now. He says he will write more during the week about how getting the news felt and what the next steps are.

-Thanks be to Jaysus for tha, cos I need to go jacks now for a piss. I need to have a pint and a fag to calm me auld nerves.

-I know, put the bleedin heart crossways on ya.

-Tha it would. Be better to get these tests done than go around with yer head in the sand or up yer arse trying to ignore it cause ye're too embarrassed to talk with a doc about it.

-Yeah, tha's for sure. Ok, I'm off now.

-Til next time then.

-Til then...

CHAPTER 3

Head Wreck

20 August 2017

-So, wha's the story this week?

-Ah, ya know yerself.

-Nah, I don't. Otherwise I wouldn't have fuckin asked!

-Well, he's been bleedin goin on.

-'Bout wha?

-Us! He says he can't sleep with the racket we are makin in his head.

-Fuck, tha's gratitude for ya! Bustin our bollocks here, tryin to get his message out 'bout his journey with prostate cancer and he's the fuckin nerve to say we are the problem!

-Ah, I think he's just feelin the pressure this week. Sure, it'll be grand.

-I hear he's been talkin with his Mum a lot lately.

-Yeah, but sure she's dead three years now.

-Oh, so can he talk with the dead?

-He says it's like non-iron shirts.

-Wha? Come a-fuckin-gain what the shite has non-iron shirts got to do with talkin to the dead?

-In his twisted dyslexic head, it makes sense, he maintains all shirts are non-iron, ya just decide whether ya want to fuckin iron them or not! LOL!

-Don't do tha!

-Do wha?

-LOL. We're not fuckin voices in a millennial kid's head, this is not ROG's diary. Fuckin D4 Southsider. Gettin back to talkin with the dead, how does he do tha?

-Easy, we can all talk to the dead. It's only if they answer back we have a problem!

-Right, so he's not a psycho or anything?

-Psychic, ya gobshite.

-Yeah, tha too!

-No, he's not. He just likes to talk thru things in his mind.

-So, how was the week then?

-He got some therapy.

-Oh, ya mean he went to see a counsellor?

-No, he went to see Glen Hansard in concert at Vicar Street on Monday and reckons it was the best therapy ever. Glen beat the shite out of tha guitar of his and sang his fuckin guts out for three hours.

-Top man is Glen.

-Too fuckin right. Best bit, it gave yer man a boost as he luvs his music, ya know? Luvs it.

-Indeedo, can't sing a fuckin note or play a cord but luvs his music.

-Sure, he'd want to, livin next door to the banjo feckin queen of karaoke.

-Ah, top woman, ya know! Best neighbours ever, there when ya need them, fuck off when ya don't.

-True for ya.

-Anyways, yer man Stephen James Smith was support to Glen. Jaysus, wha a man! Fuckin marvellous poet, recited *Dublin* and *My Ireland*.

-Right, I hear he claims to be from the Liberties but with a fuckin name like tha, who's he kiddin? Fuckin Stephen James Smith – sounds more D4 to me than Liberties!

-I hear ya.

-He looked fucked at end of this week. Jaysus, looks like a guy who got caught in middle of Mayweather and McGregor.

-Yeah, looks like shit after a storm but doin better today.

-So, wha had him so fucked up.

-Think it was a tough week mentally for him. The whole idea of cancer in his body and then the entire family comin to terms with it. Ya know, it plays on yer fuckin mind even though he knows it's not terminal, ya can't help but think where else is it in yer body.

-Poor fucker! Jaysus, ye're right, it affects the entire family too.

-Ah, but they're a great bunch. The daughters are wonderful, givin him plenty of auld hugs.

-Fair play to them. Not easy for them either, seein their Da go through this, not easy. Fuckin illness affects everyone around ya, but sure, he will kick this to the kerb cause he can and he will.

-Top man. Sure, I see the Rudd text him, 'My Captain'. Tha gave him a little boost.

-Yeah, wha's tha all about? Were they in the army together or wha?

-No fuckin way! Can ya see yer man joinin the army with tha mop of hair – like a crow's nest on his head! Nah, it's from the movie *Dead Poets Society*. Just their little thing they have. Anyways, says he is not gettin his hair cut til he gets rid of this. Neil Young eat yer heart out!

-Ah, right. So, wha was the reaction from all tha know him?

-Ah, great! Got lots of messages and best wishes – support is all important, ya know. Cos this illness can get into yer fuckin head.

-Yeah, ya even hear voices!

-Smart fuck.

-Well, what was it all 'bout this week?

-Mainly an emotional one. Yer head fuckin ya up, kinda week.

-Got tha alright.

-Lots of concerns about how his health, his diagnosis will impact on his business. Ya know he runs the company? Well, if he's not earning, how will they generate revenue? So, a bit more pressure on him than if he was workin with a big company who wouldn't really feel the impact of his absence thru illness.

-Ah, but ya know he's been thru worse and come thru the other side. He will get thru this too.

-Deffo, and as he always says, we have the bad days to make us realise how great the good ones truly are.

-Jaysus, tha's clever! Right little feckin philosopher, ain't he?

-Look at ya! Did ya swallow a dictionary for breakfast this morning?

-Fuck ya.

-Ooh, someone's touchy!

-I'll give ya a fuckin touch of me fist in a minute if ya don't shut yer bleedin gob!

-So, what's next?

-Bone scan on Tuesday.

-Will tha hurt?

-Nah, just a needle to insert radioactive dye into yer body then couple hours later have the scan, then off home.

-Great, any side effects?

-Just don't be around children or pregnant women for 24hrs.

-So, will the Missus not be sleepin with him then?

-Think she's gone beyond gettin preggers!

-Right so.

-Then Thursday he attends his graduation for MSc in Project & Programme Management.

-Ooh la la! Thought ya said he was Dyslexic and mildly Autistic?

-He is but tha doesn't mean ye're stupid or can't achieve.

-Game ball! Anythin else to say?

-Yeah, one thing's been buggin him.

-Wha, is it? The radiotherapy, robotic surgery, side effects, wha?

-Nah, why does his urologist consultant have a door tha's over eight feet high? Plus hangin on the wall in the waiting room, an abstract painting tha looks like someone's balls were dipped in paint and then squeezed up against the canvas!

-Jaysus, is he for real? Some fucked up guy…

-He reckons the archimatect got the measurements all arseways.

-Well, I'm gonna head on.

-Sure, I'll go with ya.

-Not like ya can stay here without me, now is it?

-Always tryin to be the smartarse fecker, aren't ya?

-Til next time then.

-Til then…

CHAPTER 4

⸙

Selection Box

28 August 2017

-What happened to yer man?

-Wha ya mean?

-He never wrote anythin on Sunday mornin, was he sick or wha?

-Nah, had friends visitin from Umpa Lumpa land.

-Where the feck is tha?

-States. Ya know where tha little orange guy who shouts fire and fury comes from? The guy tha thinks he's white – the only fuckin white supremacist I have ever known tha tries so hard to change the colour of his skin.

-Tha's the US market fucked! We will have no sales there now!

-So, what's the craic with him?

-He went for the bone scan like we mentioned last week. Piece of cake. Simple injection into the arm to send the radioactive dye around the body, then go off for three hours. Come back and lie on a bed where the CT Scan does the business. All over in forty minutes.

-Jaysus. Tha's a piece of piss. No bother to him, so.

-Indeed. Best bit was the hospital phoned early next morning to say all was clear. Cancer is contained in prostate.

-Ah, for feck sake! He must have been over the moon with tha news?

-Dancin inside with joy, he was. Even the Missus was excited!

-Most excitement she's got out of him in months so, if ya know what I mean!

-Yeah, I know wha ya mean but his mind is fucked at the mo.

-Guess so, give him tha. But funny, isn't it?

-Jaysus. Ye've some twisted mind if ya think havin any form of cancer is fun!

-Nah, ya eejit! I mean they're over the moon with bein content he just has cancer in the prostate, but he still has the fuckin thing.

-He said it's like been told their goin to amputate both yer legs, then they tell ya it's only yer pinky toe tha's gettin the chop.

-I said it before and I say it again, he has some warped feckin mind, this guy, comin up with an example like tha.

-I hear the mammy-in-law heard about the writin he's doin.

-Yeah, don't think she was impressed or understands. Ya know the way she is – thinks ya should tell no one yer business.

-Sure, isn't tha the point of it? Tha he tells his story so others know what happens and it removes the silence tha has been built up around it?

-Ah, she's a grand woman! Anyways, just her generation, they don't get this openness lark. She's really worried about him.

-Ya only said tha cause ye're afraid her son will read this to her.

-Too bloody right I am!

-Come here, I hear yer man from Windsor phoned.

-Wha, I thought he retired?

-Who ya talkin bout?

-The guy from Windsor, Philip?

-No, ya gobshite! The bro-in-law.

-Fuck. Is he still alive? Thought he died years ago. Haven't seen nor heard of him in yonks.

-Better still, his own bro in Birmingham phoned.

-Jaysus. The poor bloke must have thought he had terminal cancer with those two suddenly gettin on the blower, wha?

-Think he got more of a shock from those calls than when he got the news off the doc. Kept askin his Missus wha she was keepin from him, cos it must be worse if they phoned!

-He mentioned everyone keeps sayin how brave he is but he said he's not. He has cancer and there is shag all he can do 'bout it as he didn't have a choice. But if he had asked to be injected with cancer just so he could experience it and write a book to share with others, now tha would be brave.

-Nah, tha would have just been fuckin stupid!

-So, what's happened this week?

-All about selectin treatment this week.

-What're the options?

-Well, because his is advanced cancer, two options are out. They are Active Surveillance and Watchful Waiting. But for those tha do have those options, it basically means they monitor ya as prostate cancer can often grow slowly but not so in yer man's case.

-What are the treatments he can look into?

-Brachytherapy, which is basically internal radiotherapy. They place anything from 60 to 120 radioactive seeds inside yer prostate and they stay there permanently. After twelve months the seeds are no longer active.

-For fuck sake! Tha sounds painful.

-All done under anaesthetic and ye're up and about in couple of days but ya must keep arm's length from children under twelve years for two months.

-Ah right, fair play so.

-Ya can also get external radiotherapy. No anaesthetic and usually only fifteen-minute blasts at a time. Ye're not radioactive after it, so can be around children.

-Sound, is he goin for tha then?

-Hasn't decided yet. Has to see radiotherapist on Wednesday and surgeon on Thursday.

-So, he can also have surgery?

-Yeah, three options.

-Very nice, when decidin can he phone a friend, do a 50:50 or ask the audience?

-Smart now, aren't ya?

-So, wha are the surgical options?

-Open prostatectomy surgery.

-What the feck is tha when it's at home?

-Open surgery.

-Well, it's not goin to be closed, now is it, for feck sake?

-Do ya want to know wha they are or are ya goin to try be a smart fuck all night?

-Ok, I'll shut me gob.

-Laparoscopic prostatectomy or, as we know it, keyhole surgery.

-Deffo hole surgery anyways. Would tha be the front or back door the key goes into? Ha ha ha!

-I'm feckin warnin ya...

-Ok, I'll shut up!

-Finally, there is robot-assisted laparoscopic prostatectomy or robotic surgery.

-Better known as WALL-E surgery! Ha ha ha! When will we know what he chooses?

-Hopefully by weekend.

-Grand so. I guess they all come with possible side effects?

-Yeah, they do but as the doc said, if ya were to read the side effects of paracetamol ya would never put one in yer mouth!

-True for ya.

-I hear Gimli was on the blower to him.

-Ah, he was indeedo. Sound bloke. Ya know, all fire and brimstone but heart of gold underneath it all.

-Sure, they go back years and years.

-They do indeed. He mentioned he was feelin tired and Gimli said only to be expected because the mental stress it puts on ya is exhausting.

-Ah Jaysus! Tha makes perfect sense and here was I thinkin it was the cancer tiring him out.

-I see his Da has not only managed to get on FB at age eighty-three but even figured out where the 'Like' button is! Ha ha ha!

-Fuck sake. Will ya be careful! He'll be readin this too!

-Ah sure, no harm. He knows we are only takin the piss. Anyways, I see he found his two cousins from England too?

-Never knew he lost them.

-Tha's it! I warned ya! Ye're too fuckin smart tonight. I'm off.

-Ok, so. Best say good night then.

-Til next time then.

-Til then...

CHAPTER 5

Dr Joy

3 September 2017

-How's it goin?

-Grand. Yeah, fair to middlin.

-I see he's back walkin with his mate Enda.

-Ah sure begorra, they were up with the lark this mornin, out and 'bout in Punchestown. Doin the lap like the fillies.

-Grand soft mornin for it.

-Ah, to be sure.

-Come here for ya.

-Wha?

-Why we fuckin talkin like two auld culchies?

-Jaysus, ye're right! Must have been all tha fresh air gone to his head.

-I've a question before we start.

-What's tha then?

-We are the voices in yer man's head, right?

-Correcto.

-Then we are not real.

-Hmmm... Well, we are – as I am me and yous are yous.

-Exactly! What if yer man is the voice in our heads and we are not imaginary? What if he's fuckin us up so much tha we can't recognise the fact he is the imaginary voice here?

-Ah, tha's just too feckin confusin for me... I mean tha's gettin really deep now!

-I know but remember he said he couldn't sleep cos of the racket we were makin in his head? Well, now I can't sleep either because I am so confused if I am me or I am him! And if I am him, then who are yous?

-Ah now, let's not go down tha path. Wonder if Doyler's lads have the same issue?

-Anyways. Wha was the story this week?

-Went to tha radiotherapist or as he calls her – Dr Joy.

-Why does he call her tha?

-Cause she's fuckin full of joyous news once ye're not the victim – sorry, I mean patient.

-Ah I see, what was the visit like then?

-Well, they were in with her for over ninety minutes. Usual start, ya know like, how ya doin, wha ya know about prostate cancer and then she takes out her little model of a prostate and all sorts of picture diagrams.

-I hear the wife was with him this time and the little grandson too.

-They were. Sure, like his shadow where he goes, she goes.

-How did tha go down?

-'Bout twenty minutes into the meetin yer wan, Dr Joy says, 'Right. Now let me examine ya up on the couch.'

-Ah Jaysus! Not the fuckin rubber gloves and gel again!

-Ya got it! Only this time she says, 'I might not be able to feel it as my fingers are very small.'

-Ah no!

-Yeah, and sure enough she has tiny fingers but tha didn't stop her havin a go!

-Bet the wife loved bein in there for tha.

-Payback for all those smear tests she has to get.

-How was the little man?

-Ah Jaysus! In the middle of it, yer man lets out a small noise cause it was like yer wan was drilling for oil with no chance of hittin the seabed with those small fingers. And the little man shouts out, 'Are you ok, Pappy?'

-Get out of it!

-Then when Dr Joy is finished and walks back to her chair, he runs over and pulls the curtain back.

-Classic! So wha did she have to say?

-Ah, she's thrown the kitchen sink at him. He's to get surgery, hormone treatment, radiotherapy and chemo.

-For fuck sake, is tha normal?

-Nah, most guys just need surgery and tha's it but his is a nasty little bugger.

-Come here, ya said hormone treatment. What's tha 'bout?

-Ah Jaysus, get ready for this. Ya'll need to sit down and try not wince... castration through prescription!

-OH MY FUCKIN GOD! Wha? Why?

-Ah sure, she's full of feckin good news this one. She tells him 'bout twenty years ago for cases like him, they considered surgical castration but it caused a lot of mental issues for men tha got it.

-Duh! Way to go Einstein. No fuckin joke.

-Yeah, but now with the hormone treatment, it does the same thing. It stops the testosterone bein generated and then when he comes off the medication everything reverts back to normal.

-Bollocks or is tha bollix? So, wha's next?

-Well, he went to visit the urologist the followin day and he made sense of the whole lot. He's to go see WALL-E the robotic surgeon late September and then they will schedule surgery for October.

-Ah ok, then does he get radiotherapy immediately after?

-Nah, all depends on the surgery and wha they find out when they analyse the walnut once they have it out and in the lab.

-So, when does radiotherapy start?

-Well, he has to be finished with the tube up the prick and get rid of the bag first.

-WHAT??

-Yeah, when ya get yer prostate out, ya need a bag for a short time after. When ya get yer bladder workin again on yer own, only then can they commence radiotherapy.

-Some journey ahead so?

-Yeah but one step at a time. He needs to just concentrate on surgery first, then gettin rid of the bag. After tha, we'll look at next phase – if there is another phase. Surgery might do the business.

-Game ball. How's the Missus and family copin?

-I think they are all livin in a daze, including himself. Some days better than others but at times he said they feel like they're in a dream and this is not real.

-Ha ha ha! Well, we both know how tha feels!

-I hear he called up to the bro-in-law other day.

-Yeah, first time meetin relatives outside immediate family. He said it felt a bit like comin out of the closet, if ya get wha he means.

-Ah yeah, get tha.

-Sometimes he says he feels like the walkin dead, even though his cancer ain't terminal but some poor fuckers get terminal cancer from this prostate shit.

-Get tha.

-But bro-in-law and his Missus were lovely, plus the nieces and nephew. Difficult for everyone. I mean, wha do ya say? 'Hear you got cancer?' – not a great conversation opener.

-Ah, it'll be fine. It'll get better as time goes by.

-Sure thing. Yer wan, Dr Joy reckons three year journey ahead of him before cancer free.

-Jaysus, tha's a long time, but look on bright side – they expect him to live three years! Ha ha ha!

-Ye're full of wit...

-I know, sure tha's why I got this gig. Come here, tell me will he be able to work in between?

-Yeah, no worries there. Just a few months after surgery. Plus, da tube in his dick for a week after the surgery. Sure, there are some poor guys left with the tube permanently... Life goes on.

-How's his mood?

-Ask his Missus. Think her and the daughters are ready to trade him in. Good days and bad days but they just give him space on the bad days as he is a bit of a loner like tha, likes his space. Always has been, even as a child. Sometimes the world closes in, brings him back to when he was a child with the dyslexia and all, he likes to escape to his own world.

-Ah right so, but fair fuckin play to him bein so open and honest in this book. Most lads I know would not admit these things and would try to hide them. But I guess if he doesn't say it as it is, this book is worth fuck all to anyone.

-Now ye've got it, tis all 'bout helpin others who will come after him. Tha's why he wants as many people as possible to read the book so he can spread the word.

-Or does he just want them to buy the book to fill his pockets? I mean come on!

-Nah, not the case with this book. 100% of all profits made from the book sales go to the Marie Keating Foundation. Sure, he donated the bleeding thing to them! Me thinks this was his way of tryin to get shut of us two but little does he know we're goin nowhere!

-Jaysus, fair play to our bro. He is a sound bloke.

-Ok, so is tha it for this week?

-Yeah, think so. He has a bit to talk about on pelvic exercises, etc. but thinks with the introduction of castration this week he better let all the guys go off and get some colour back into their cheeks, as right now they are all lookin a little grey.

-Just before we go...

-Yeah, wha?

-This whole thing 'bout terminal cancer and illnesses...

-Yeah, wha 'bout it?

-Do ya know wha I think 'bout tha?

-Fuck sake, I am nearly afraid to ask, but go on. Wha do ya think?

-Well, I reckon we are all terminal as every life ends at some point and it's just tha those who have been told they are terminal have the opportunity to spend those last few weeks, months or years makin the most out of life. Whereas the rest of us eejits walk around thinkin it will never happen to us just yet and spend our feckin lives chasin happiness in things tha will never bring us contentment.

-Hold the fuckin credits there! Ye're goin too feckin deep now and puttin the soppy into philo-soppy-cal on me.

-Ah, I know but ya know there is some fuckin truth in tha.

-There is but doesn't stop the heartache when ye're told ya are terminal.

-Deffo, I am not tryin to say tha but remember when he was told his Ma was terminal?

-Which time? The feckin docs kept tellin the poor woman she was dyin but she refused!

-Some woman, hey? I mean the time they got it right and said she had five weeks to live.

-Well, I guess they were eventually goin to get it right one day.

-But yeah, I do. Ground opened up beneath him. He adored his Ma.

-Still does.

-No arguin on tha here.

-Ok. Well, I am off for a pint of the black stuff. I need it after this. Ya comin?

-Sure thing, right behind ya.

-Til next time then.

-Til then...

CHAPTER 6

❦

Ed

7 October 2017

-Howzit?

-Wha?

-Howzit, ya know, how is it goin?

-Jaysus, what the feck are ya talkin with a South African accent for?

-Shit, never realised tha! It's this fecker, he's playin mind games with us again. Think he must have been thinkin of his peeps out there in SA when he started to write this.

-His peeps? Who the fuck does he think he is, Mandela?

-Well, ya know wha they said in The Commitments, '*The Irish are the blacks of Europe. And Dubliners are the blacks of Ireland. And the Northside Dubliners are the blacks of Dublin. So say it once and say it loud, I'm black and I'm proud.*'

-Fuck sake! There ya go again. I'm tellin ya, Doyler will deffo sue the arse off him now!

-Yeah right, Doyler would have to read this first before he does tha and the chances of tha happenin are the same chances as me meetin Bowie.

-But sure, Bowie is dead.

-Exactly.

-So, where exactly has he been the last month? Thought he was writin this weekly?

-Ah, lots happenin. He was away in France for a week in mid-September. Here, ya never believe what they call prostate cancer in France.

-Go on then, wha?

-Cancer de la prostate!

-Huh, what the fuck? Sure, it's no different.

-Ah, but did ya say it with the French accent?

-Feck. Ye're right. Sounds different now, but ya do know no one readin this hears us talk?

-Yeah, I know tha but I bet they all said it out loud with a French accent!

-Jaysus. How do we do tha? We're now screwin up their heads too! Anyways, what's the story with the prostate, is it still there or wha?

-Well, where the fuck do ya think it would be? Not exactly a gallstone, he can't shit or piss it out of him, is it!

-There ya go rantin, 'is it'. STOP with the SA slang! Ok then, what's goin on?

-Well, he went to see WALL-E the robotic surgeon.

-How did tha go?

-Yeah, grand. Went through the whole thing how he will have six small incisions across his stomach where they will place the instruments through, one incision will be slightly bigger so they can get the prostate out, be in the shape of a 'C' across his stomach just above the belly button

-Right, so it's the male version of a C-Section so?

-Jaysus, tha's a good one. Never thought of tha.

-Then wha?

-Well, he has to stay in hospital for two nights. They operate Monday and he will be home on a Wednesday or Thursday.

-Feck, tha's great.

-Yeah, he'll have the bag in for a week.

-Stop the fuckin bus. Wha bag? Ya never mentioned tha?

-Ya know, the bag for the piss? He will have a small tube goin up his prick and into his bladder and it empties into a bag he straps to his leg.

-Fuck sake. Will it be on for long?

-Nah, just for seven or eight days after his operation.

-Sound as a pound, not long so. Once he gets it off, is the water works all workin fine then?

-Not really, he will be wearin sanitary pads for a while. Could last six to twelve months with some people.

-Poor fuck, how does he feel about tha?

-Says it's better than havin the bag for six to twelve months.

-Tha's for sure.

-But either way, once the cancer is out, who cares? At least ye're still fuckin alive and can spend time with yer loved ones.

-Exacto, true for ya.

-He also went to see Nurse Jackie. Ah, tha was some fuckin fun.

-Why's tha?

-She showed him the bag and how tha works. Then she got on to the feckin excitin bit. It was like bein on the set of a porno movie, reviewing the special effects.

-Go on then, tell me more.

-She says to him, 'Ya know, you may suffer with ED after surgery.'

-Who the feck is Ed and why should he suffer with him? Will they be sharin a room or wha?

-ED is Erectile Dysfunction.

-Ah Jaysus!

-But it's cool. He's been sufferin with tha for near on four years now.

-So, wha can they do for him?

-Ah Jaysus! Tha was the fun bit – he asked can he still just take the stiff pills!

-And...

-Nope, no good.

-Huh? Ya mean he will be a limpy for the rest of his life?

-This is where he had fun and all sense of shyness went out the feckin window!

-How?

-Well, Nurse Jackie says the pill won't work but ya can get a pump, then the Missus chirps in, 'Yes love, I read about them and you can get them online.'

-No fuckin way!

-Hold it there! Nurse Jackie jumps in and says, 'No, you can't get these ones online.' She asks, 'Have you met Rodrigo? He deals with this aspect, but here is a sample of what it looks like.'

-Jaysus, wha did it look like?

-A fuckin elephant semen collector! Ha ha ha!

-Ah go on, will ya!

-Wait for it though... Nurse Jackie then says, 'They have to be custom made and Rodrigo will measure you for it.'

-Noooooooooo!!

-Yeah, and he says, 'Do they come in extra small?'

-Ah Jaysus! Wha next?

-Now get this, she said, 'Were you told tha it may get smaller after the operation, as they have to move things about?'

-This just keeps gettin better! Was he on the floor at this stage?

-He just burst out laughin! Then he said he might as well become a Lady Boy if things get much worse. The Missus asked was there anything else they could try.

-Quick tell me, cos I think mine has just retreated up inside me at this stage.

-Calm as ya like, Nurse Jackie says, 'You can always use the injection.'

-WHAT?

-Yeah, ya inject into yer prick to enlarge it. Yer man's Missus says, 'Won't tha hurt?' As quick as anything, Nurse Jackie says, 'No its just a small prick.'

-No way! Ha ha ha!

-Best bit was yer man says, 'How do you know I have a small prick?' and then they all burst out laughin!

-So, it was a good visit then?

-Well, he had a laugh. He told Nurse Jackie he was writin this book and she thought it was a good idea. She even asked for a copy so she could share it around and hopefully help others.

-So, what's next?

-In for surgery next, as I said earlier. So, not sure if he will write much over next week.

-Yeah, get tha.

-But he will record how he felt, etc.

-So, is tha it then?

-Nah, he had a personal FB message from a good friend of his and she said she hoped he was managin to maintain inwardly the amazing attitude he was showin outwardly.

-Well, is he?

-Ya know, he is not superman. He does get down. He gets annoyed it happened to him, but he thinks how lucky he is too.

-How did he make tha out? Sure, he got sepsis from his first biopsy last December which gave him five infections!

-Well, his Missus and him reckon he was very fortunate to get the sepsis, as the biopsy last December showed up no cancer. If he hadn't got so sick, they would never have discovered just how bad he truly was.

-But was he not annoyed he got cancer when he never smoked or drank alcohol in his life?

-Again, he says he was lucky. Imagine if he had drunk and smoked with this aggressive cancer gene? He reckons he could be dead by now!

-Jaysus, some fuckin twisted sense of rationale he uses but fair play to him. I suppose a positive attitude is half the battle.

-Indeedo. Sure, as he says, every breath we take from the day we are born is one less and closer to our final one. It's not the amount of years we live but the quality of those years and what we do with them.

-Ah come on, man! Don't get all philosophical again on us now! But he's right.

-Ok, I'm off now.

-Yeah so am I, goin to go get a measuring tape to measure mine.

-Why the fuck ya doin tha?

-I just want it recorded so if I ever get prostate cancer, I will know how much it shrank.

-Well, I've a ten-millimetre ruler, if ya want it...

-Fuck ya!

-Til next week then.

-Til then...

CHAPTER 7

Male C-Section

15 October 2017

-I hear he's not laughin much these days.

-Well, would ya be laughin after havin yer prostate removed only a week ago and yer shaggin stomach feels like ya have triplets kickin the shite out of ya from the inside out?

-Come here, do ya think this whole prostate malarkey is somehow due to women's rights and equality? Tha their now gettin their own back on us?

-Who the fuck knows but for those religious types, it solves the time auld argument tha yer man upstairs is a man! Jaysus, whatever sex tha higher power is, it's certainly not something from our planet.

-I hear even havin a dump feckin hurts now?

-I think he now has a new understandin of what his two daughters went through when they had their C-sections.

-Tha's for sure! Here, do ya recall when his Missus had their first child? She woke up the day after in hospital and it was so bleedin dark she couldn't see properly, and she put pile cream on her toothbrush instead of toothpaste!!

-Well, if she was talkin shite beforehand tha would deffo explain it! Ha ha ha!

-Ah, good one! Ye're as sharp as a pencil today.

-Well, a pared one, for sure. Anyways, it's not like yer man has any lead left in his pencil!

-Be careful, he'll hear ya.

-Don't think there is any chance of him not hearin me, now, is there? We are in his feckin noggin.

-Ya know, he thinks he has made a scientific discovery.

-Almost afraid to ask but go on, wha is it?

-He reckons the walnut is connected to yer tear ducts.

-Wha shite are ya on 'bout now? Yer prostate connected to yer tear ducts? For fuck sake! Yer eyes are not in yer arse. Although mind ya, with yous, I wonder at times.

-Well, he reckons he's very weepy these days.

-True but sure, he was diagnosed with cancer, got sepsis, had numerous infections and some hospitalised him. Then, he just had his prostate sucked out of him by a bleedin robotic arm and he's surprised he's weepy. Tha's enough to bring tears to anyone's eyes.

-Guess so but he says he feels very emotional at times and he wells up too.

-Just keep him away from all those feckin tear jerk movies.

-Well now, tears are the only thing he will be jerkin out so let's let him have tha at least!

-Bit weird all the same.

-Wha is?

-Ya know, how d'ya have a dump with a bleedin tube hangin out of yer dick? I mean normally ya have a good auld piss before the dumpin starts.

-Guess so but wha's the alternative?

-I am just sayin, tha's all.

-Ok, then it's a bit weird. Ya happy now?

-Wouldn't say happy but sure, who is?

-He will be glad to make the trip to the hospital tomorrow and get this tube out of him and be rid of the bag.

-Ya, he's walkin like a pirate with a peg leg when it fills and gets so heavy.

-Ah, all will be grand tomorrow so. He'll be flyin around after tha visit.

-Been some trip these past few months and the last week, sure, tha's been epic in a not so great way.

-Yeah, epic is a word ya could use alright. I would have said it's been an utter cluster fuck!

-Well, ya would, ya fecker.

-Do ya honestly think anyone will get this book? Ya know, understand wha he is tryin to achieve?

-Who knows but fuckin hope so as otherwise we have wasted our feckin time and could have just spent it annoyin the shite out of him.

-It's a bit out there though, bit Yoko Ono like.

-Yeah, like the time she had an art exhibition in New York with no art. She said ya just had to use yer imagination.

-Or the time she had the step ladder with a magnifying glass hangin from the ceiling, when ya climbed up and read the message it just said, 'Yes'.

-Only difference is he's not smokin the weed.

-Bet he wished he had now, sure living tha healthy life did fuck all for him.

-Depends.

-Depends on wha?

-Well, he could have done all tha and possibly would have got terminal cancer instead of aggressive cancer.

-Fuck tha. All cancer is aggressive cos I have never heard of meek cancer.

-Alright. I'm done.

-Yeah, same here.

-Til next time then.

-Til then...

CHAPTER 8

***

Willie Leaks

4 November 2017

-He's back then?

-Yeah, appears so.

-What's this one about then?

-Not certain, we will have to see how it goes.

-Wha's he doin now?

-Dunno, he seems to have stopped writing.

-Is he ok?

-To be honest I'm not sure, He's gone very quiet.

-So, wha do we do now then?

-Just keep shtum for the mo and see where it takes us.

-He had the op, ya know, on 9 October.

-Yeah, he was in theatre for six hours.

-Feck, I never knew he could act. Wha was he playin in?

-Nah, ya gobshite! Theatre, the operating theatre, ya know?

-Ah, I get ya!

-Wait, here he comes. Seems to be some movement now.

-Ya know tha Nurse Jackie one? She told him writin this book is good for him.

-Sure, it's very telepathic for him, isn't it?

-TELEPATHIC! Wha the fuck do ya mean, telepathic?

-Ya know like, good to get it all out.

-Jaysus. Ya mean therapeutic?

-Yeah, tha's wha I said.

-Well, they say it's good to talk and write yer feelings down.

-Do ya think he's a bit of an extortionist with writin this book?

-Wha ya mean now? Is he charging people to read it? Cos feck him if he is – we are gettin no money for our efforts!

-No, I mean do ya think he is simply lookin for attention, notice like?

-Ah, for feck sake man, who is the dyslexic here? Ya mean exhibitionist. No, I don't think he is. He just genuinely wants to spread the word about #prostatecancer and get people chattin 'bout it.

-I see what ya did there, slippin tha hashbrown in.

-Hashtags, ya fuckin moron. HASHTAGS!

-How did surgery go then?

-All good, he went in on a Monday. Started operating on him at one thirty and out after six thirty.

-How was he goin in?

-Yeah, all good. Can't remember much after bein brought in on trolley to a small room where anaesthetist prepped him – he got small injection, and next thing he knew, he was bein woken up in recovery room. Then, later tha night, brought back to his own room.

-Wha was it like, ya know after, was he in pain?

-He says during tha night he woke a few times but was not in too much pain but felt more discomfort and strangely he kept tellin the nurse he needed to wee.

-Ah poor fuck. Could he not pass his wee?

-Nah, he could as he had the tube goin up his....

-Careful now. Choose yer word carefully as ya know the Missus gave out 'bout him usin the prick word last time and his Da too.

-Ok, I won't say prick then. I will say he had a tube up his flute.

-Yeah, tha will please them. So, with the tube up his flute, how does tha work? Will it not fall out when he moves?

-Nah, it goes into his bladder and they blow it up so it stops it slippin out, it feeds into a bag and then ya simply empty the urine in the morning.

-Right, and did he have to wear it during the day too?

-Sure thing. Ya get a small bag to wear during the day so ya can walk around and it straps onto yer leg. Then at night ya get a bigger bag tha sits into a stand on the floor. Ya know, so ya don't need to get up during the night to empty it.

-Was he in hospital for long?

-Got out on the Wednesday at noon. Here ya know on the Tuesday morning after the op, they had him up out of bed and in gettin a shower. A lovely auld dear, Maid Marianne, helped him and hosed him down.

-For feck sake, with urine bag in tow?

-Yep, plus he had one other bag comin out of his side tha was for drainage to drain any blood away.

-Ah, here! Now I feel sick, was tha not all a bit sore?

-Nah, they took away the drainage bag after he showered. It was fine.

-Wha 'bout the pee one, when did tha go?

-The followin Monday as they have to keep it in for a full week. Actually, it was the day of storm Ophelia.

-Jaysus, did they go out in tha?

-He said nothing was stoppin him gettin the bag out.

-So, how did tha go?

-Well, the male nurse Rodrigo took it out.

-Go on then, was it sore? Someone pullin a tube out of yer flute tha was all the way up to yer bladder?

-Nah, no pain, more discomfort.

-So, the big question is does he have leakage?

-LEAKAGE. Those docs are havin a bleeden laugh! It's a fuckin tsunami. As soon as the tube was taken out and he stood up, he filled the entire pad. Says he now walks with a waddle like Donald Duck.

-I hear his Missus jeers him and says he has a fine lookin pack down there with all the padding!

-Indeedo. She's a gas woman and his biggest confidante through all this.

-I have to ask, did it shrink like they said it would?

-Shrink? First time he went to the loo, he wanted to phone the police to report a missing penis!

-Ah Jaysus. Was he sore down there in the lunchbox?

-Let's just say tha even the Notorious McGregor has never had bruisin in his lunchbox like this guy had.

-Oh fuck! Was he on lots of painkillers?

-He actually survived on paracetamol and an anti-inflammatory.

-How long was he on those for then?

-Supposed to be a week post op but he had a very bad day the Tuesday after they took the bag off him.

-Wha happened?

-He had finished the meds, and on the Tuesday, his back passage to his bowel went into spasm as he suffers with IBS. This was his first real bad day and he couldn't get his bowel to move til seven tha night. He broke down during the day and cried like a little baby a number of times.

-Ah no, but it's good to let it all out and cryin can actually help.

-Well anyways, he also takes a very mild laxative to soften things up and is still on tha but came off all pain meds two weeks after the op.

-Some man to manage all tha on just paracetamol. Did he have any more wobbles?

-Yep, he had a lot of pain when due to have bowel movement for a further week but then during week four, tha all subsided so he only has minor cramps now when he needs to go and slight pain after, which is gone within fifteen minutes or so.

-Well, ya know they all want to ask 'bout the incontinence. So, what's the story with the water works?

-Work in progress. Does his pelvic floor muscle exercises every day as required but still no control once he stands up. But good news is, he has full control lyin down, sittin down and not too bad walkin. Just initial standin causes gravity to kick in and drain him out.

-How is he copin with tha, then?

-Ah, it's hard. In fact, it's the most difficult part. For the most part, he can cope but then there is the odd day where he just caves in and has a cry.

-I get tha. Must be bloody awful.

-His little grandson stayed over for Halloween and next morning they both had their night pull-up pants in a nappy bag ready for the bin. In fact, he calls tha the walk of shame – every morning he walks to the bin with all his bags in hand from the pull-up pants he has to wear.

-Yeah, can only imagine but ya know, no one would mind or say anything to him.

-Nah, he knows tha and has the best neighbours ever. In fact, one day he was having a really bad day, so he was lying down on the bed and his neighbour next door was out sweepin up the leaves.

-Which neighbour?

-The Karaoke Queen. Anyways as she was sweepin the leaves up, she started hummin a tune. He simply closed his eyes and it felt like she was singin him a lullaby. It was so comforting and magical tha he filled up with tears.

-I hear he does tha a lot now, fill up with tears.

-Yep, silly little things now overpower him and not just from sadness but joy too. The little one next door had a baby and he loves lookin at the pics she posts on FB. Then for no reason, he gets all emotional at times just lookin at them. Class neighbours, the whole lot of them. It's not where ya live tha counts but who ya live next door to.

-Ok, I have to ask this one too. Ya know wha they said about ya know the morning glory when ya wake, is it truly gone? Is he now a limpy?

-Afraid so. No more raisin the mast first thing in the morning. All gone.

-Ah man! Does tha not define a male, like who we are? Wha do ya do when tha has lost its stature?

-Stature? Will ya listen to ya! Think of it this way, he is still alive and ya know there is more to a relationship than stickin it in, gruntin for five minutes – two in yer case, and then lyin back and sayin, 'Well, was tha as good for yous, honey?'

-I suppose... I guess forward play comes more into the scene now.

-Jaysus. Would ya ever go to English classes! Foreplay, ya asshole, not forward play. He's not trying to play a game of football here, ya know!

-Ya know, he has been brutally honest in this book. Does his Missus mind as everyone knows who he is?

-Nah, she is good with it. He could hide behind a different name but wants to make this real. He is not ashamed of what has happened to him. Sure, he had no control over it. He wants men and women to read this, know the full story. No point in glossin over it and as prostate cancer is so prevalent. Men need to know wha is goin to happen but also realise there is light at the end.

-Some woman. He is a lucky man to have her by his side.

-Very much so, plus this fuckin illness affects everyone around ya and it really attacks yer mental health too. The docs can stitch ya up, etc. but it gets into yer head. I mean incontinence and erectile dysfunction, who wouldn't get issues goin on in their head with tha?

-No wonder he took four weeks to write this! Poor shite, must be killin him.

-Ah, ya know him. He laughs in public and collapses when his wife is around him but important thing is, he made a promise to himself when he started this journey.

-Wha was tha then?

-He promised he would cry if he felt like it was gettin too much, he promised he would talk openly to his Missus about EVERYTHING and all his fears, etc., but most of all, he promised he would not close her and his daughters out to how he felt.

-Fair play.

-Furthermore...

-STOP! Furthermore? Tha's not us talkin! He's feckin bombing in on our script. Ha ha ha! Get him back on track!

-Ha ha ha! Yeah, sorry 'bout tha. Also, his Da has been great. He texts him and comes down to visit him as he knows wha it's like to go through cancer.

-I hear he gets a lot of private messages too.

-Sure thing, he is so lucky to have a network of friends around him tha keep in contact with him. He knows some of them don't know how to handle the situation so don't message him but tha's cool. Everyone is different and anyways wha do ya say to a guy who is fifty-five this Christmas and is back peein in his pants and can't get an erection? No problemo there, he fully understands their situation.

-Was tha said in a Northern Ireland accent?

-Wha ya on about now?

-SITCH-E-AYSHUN

-Fuck me, ye're a funny git!

-So, we done?

-Well, there's lots more but think he has drained himself emotionally writin this, so let's leave it at tha.

-Sure thing. But can I ask one more question?

-Go on then.

-Ya know people who have an accident and say they can't see or walk anymore, they say they have dreams 'bout when they were well. Does he have them?

-Ye're basically askin does he have dreams about when his pecker worked and functioned proper?

-Yeah, is tha too personal?

-Well, warts and all, tha's what he said. He said he would write honestly, no shadows to hide in. Yep, he dreams about bein able to pee normally and also, tha he could function properly with his Missus but nothing's there when he wakes. He says his favourite time is when he wakes early. He goes to da loo about six in mornin to his empty bladder and change da pants, then he falls back to sleep for two hours. Those two hours are his magic time, he gets into a deep sleep and just momentarily when he wakes, he feels normal, like nothing happened. But then the day kicks in and Groundhog Day starts all over.

-Ah Jaysus. Here man, ya nearly have me cryin now. Fuck, I am off home now to hug the kids and tell the Missus I love her.

-Careful now, she'll think yer havin an affair tellin her tha!

-I will never take standin up pissin or my morning glory for granted again!

-Well, we best sign off, but before we do he has a Twitter account **@ aladinsane40** where he tries to tweet about this and other stuff. He wants to raise awareness around men havin to purchase these pull-up pants and also the pads, the fuckin supermarkets don't stock many and when they do, they put them down in the women's aisle. Also, he wants to start a campaign about men's toilet cubicles havin sanitary bins as what is he meant to do when he is out in public places and has to change his pads? He will be usin the hashtag **#noshameinit** So, asks everyone to follow along and use the hashtag and tag him so he can respond.

-Ok. So, tha's it for this week then?

-Til next week then.

-Til then...

CHAPTER 9

―――― ⚬⌘⚬ ――――

WALL-E

4 December 2017

-How ya?

-Yeah, good and yous?

-Fair to middlin.

-So, what's the story today?

-Well, today is exactly eight weeks since the operation. How feckin time flies while ye're enjoyin yerself... NOT!

-What's he been up to then since he last wrote a dialogue? I mean, it's been four weeks?

-Well, he was back for his six-week post-surgery check-up with WALL-E the robotic surgeon.

-How did tha go?

-Apparently, he told him what he had is stutter surgery.

-Huh? What the fuck is tha when it's at home, then?

-Ya know, say 'is' with a stutter and ya get ISIS.

-I still don't get it. Wha d'ya mean by an ISIS prostate surgery?

-WALL-E called it a 'radical prostatectomy'. D'ya get it now? ISIS, radical...

- Feckin brill, tha is! Must remember tha one, so wha else did he have to say to him?

-Well, he said tha he must remember tha his surgery was a major one and just because he only has six minor incisions around his stomach, he must realise tha wha went on inside was very traumatic as they moved things about, cut things out and repaired other bits.

-Feck sake, no wonder he had so much discomfort.

-Sure thing, ya tend to forget just how big a surgery this is.

-Did they talk about his results from the biopsy after they sent the prostate to the lab?

-Ya bet they did, as suspected it was a *Gleason 9 T3* cancer which is fairly aggressive one, but good news is it hadn't breached the prostate wall.

-So, wha the feck does tha mean in plain English?

-Basically, he will require no further treatment, just PSA bloods done every few months and they monitor him.

-But he has no prostate anymore, so why they doin a PSA test?

-Apparently, the gene in tha particular cancer will show up should it have spread anywhere else. So, if they monitor things, they'll be alerted should it return.

-Ah I see, this technology is amazin now. Who'd have thought all this could happen? Feckin marvellous all the same. I bet Dr Joy, the radiologist, was bullin as she thought she had him for three years of treatment.

-Ah in fairness, when the team met to discuss his case, she was in the room and agreed they should just monitor now.

-Come here, I hear he met with the guys from the Movember Foundation.

-Yeah, they did an interview with him and are plannin to release a wee video sometime in the future.

-Sound as a pound.

-He's determined to turn this experience into a positive one and spread the word about men's health, particularly mental health, as he keeps sayin – although the cancer is in yer pants, the effects hit hard in the head.

-Too right. Ya know, he always mentions to the Missus whenever they go out for lunch to a restaurant how the places are always full of women havin lunch out together. And this is no matter wha country they do it in.

-Yeah true enough, the auld women know how to talk 'bout their feelin's to one another but we men just clam up and never let it out.

-He calls us the emotionally constipated Irish male because we just won't talk.

-Fuck, tha's a good one! The emotionally constipated Irish male!

-Well, are things gettin better for him yet?

-In wha sense do ya mean?

-Ya know, peeing? Is he still fillin those pull-up pants he has to wear?

-Ah, for fuck sake. Wait an I tell ya, when he was with WALL-E, he mentioned to him about tha and yer man turned around and says, 'Yeah, it's normally during the six to eight weeks post-surgery tha things begin to turn for the better.'

-Ah, for feck sake. They could have told him tha earlier. So, are things turnin for the better yet?

-Well now, he is almost afraid to say they are, in case it all goes horribly wrong, but he is doin really well. He manages to have some pee left in the bladder to get rid of when he makes it to the loo.

-Ah Jaysus. Tha's just brillo!

-Sure is. He is hopin tha for Christmas he will be in a much better place.

-Why does he not like where he lives?

-Seriously, of all the voices I could have teamed up with, how the fuck did I end up with yous? In a better place mentally, insofar as he will have more control of peeing.

-Ah, why didn't ya just say tha then? It's not me, it's...

-Don't ya fuckin dare say tha line, 'it's not me, it's you'!

-I hear he gets mixed reaction from people when he tells them wha has happened?

-Yeah, first off when he says he has cancer they are sympathetic but then when he mentions it's prostate, they are almost dismissive as if tha's not a real cancer.

-Wha d'ya mean?

-Ah ya know, they say sure ya be grand no one dies from tha. But wha they don't realise is only 26% of men who are diagnosed late with prostate cancer survive so the important thing is to catch it early, as every forty-five minutes a man dies in da UK from it and over 3,300 new cases are diagnosed every year in Ireland!

-Fuck, I didn't know tha. Jaysus, I suppose we should get the PSA blood tests done too.

-Why?

-In case we have prostate cancer.

-Ya gobshite, we are only voices in his head. We don't have prostates.

-Oh right, I sometimes forget.

-Give me bleedin patience.

-Why, are ya a doctor too?

-Huh, wha the feck ya on 'bout now?

-Patients. Are ya a doctor?

-No ya idiot! Patience not patients!

-Here, he mentioned the other day about wha a load of shite this Facebook promotion crap is because Mark SuckYerFace blocks any posts he tries to promote.

-Yeah, apparently it's because he uses profanities.

-Huh, do Facebook not support tha operating system?

-Wha ya on 'bout now?

-Profanities – is tha like a special operating system?

-Jaysus! Give me strength... No, profanities mean like he uses words such as feck, fuck, gobshite, etc.

-Ah Jaysus. So, wha ya are really sayin is tha Facebook doesn't support Irish Dublin English?

-Jaysus. Never thought of tha, I guess for first time ya are right!

-Always a first time for everythin!

-Ha ha ha! I guess so.

-I hear the Missus was gettin under the weather but was cheered up by a lunch out with the Karaoke Queen and Mary Berry.

-Ah, she was indeedo. Luncheon with the ladies cheered her up no end. Great to have friends like tha.

-Also, I hear Marathon Man jumped to the rescue and helped clear away a delivery of logs he got for the auld fire to take him thru the winter.

-Yep, best neighbours ever! Be lost without them. Plus, he has been gettin messages, calls etc. from friends who are ever so good to him, just stayin in contact.

-Ah, fair play to them all.

-Indeed, people are really great when push comes to shove.

-True for ya.

-Do ya recall he was talkin 'bout been able to fly soon after surgery and goin back to work? Some optimist, hey?

-Ah in fairness, he had no idea of the impact tha something the size of a fuckin walnut could do once removed from yer body.

-Yeah, I bet and here's the thing. I also bet there are many a bloke out there who thought the same.

-I think the big issue is...

-I buy tha when I can.

-Seriously, wha ya on? I hadn't finished my sentence.

-Nah, I mean I buy the Big Issue. Helps the homeless, ya know?

-I was 'bout to say the big issue is tha there is not enough talk about this in the public. Men tend to go underground when they get it. Sure, they haven't a clue wha to expect.

-Yeah, can see tha alright.

-Well, I guess next dialogue will be closer to Christmas?

-Be sure of it.

-Amazin tha a full year has gone by since it all kicked off.

-Yeah, says he's gonna knock 2017 out of the yard this New Year's Eve!

-Ah, he deserves a great 2018.

-Sure does. Well, best pack up.

-Til next time then.

-Til then...

CHAPTER 10

Singing Thrush

28 January 2018

-Jaysus. What's been goin down with the man himself, is he still alive?

-Just stop for one second and think 'bout wha ya just said, ya eejit!

-Wha, I'm just askin is he still kickin and screamin or pushin up the feckin daisies?

-Well, if we are the voices in his head and he was dead, we couldn't be havin this feckin conversation, now could we?

-For fuck sake, we already had this convo, ye big eejit. But if we are just voices in his head, we are imaginary, and if we are imaginary then what's to stop us talkin from the other side of the grave? Got ya there, didn't I!

-Go on with ya, will ya!

-Come here will ya, I hear Brexit is goin to reduce prostate cancer deaths by 11,690 in the EU.

-Fuck. Tha's some reduction but how is Brexit havin any impact on prostate cancer deaths?

-Well, accordin to something he read the other day online it said tha a man dies every forty-five minutes in the UK from prostate cancer.

-Jaysus, tha's a feckin lot but I still don't get the reduction in deaths because of Brexit?

-Well, when the UK leaves the EU, won't deaths from prostate cancer within the EU go down by tha amount, which is over 11,000?

-Ah, for fuck sake. Ya can't say tha!

-But I just did!

-But tha's like, I dunno, just wrong to say.

-Well, then should I just think it so and if I do, sure this whole feckin book is just voices in someone's head, so wha?

-Come on then, what's been happenin with the main man himself?

-Jaysus, ye're askin me? How the hell do I know? Sure, ye're as much in his head, as I am.

-True for ya. Well, I see things are gettin a bit better. Like, he is off the pull-up pants things and now just on pads.

-Yeah, feckin delighted with tha too because the feckin things were makin him irritable.

-I don't think the pants themselves were causin him to be irritable. I think it was the idea of havin to wear them was getting him down.

-Ah, right. I get it now.

-Sure, he is only usin three pads a day and just a light one at night. So, tha's huge progress since we last wrote anything.

-Bleedin deadly.

-Although he is sufferin with thrush from havin to wear these things now for over seventeen bleedin weeks, twenty-four seven.

-Thrush? Jaysus. Wha the fuck is he up to? I know he got a pup before he went in for the operation tha he refers to as his cancer dog, but a thrush? Why didn't he just get a parrot or budgie like any normal fool? Sure, thrush are wild feckin birds! Anyone would suffer with one of them. Is it even legal to have a thrush?

-Shut up, ya feckin gobshite! Not the bleedin bird, but the infection ya can get on yer pecker from wearin the pads and them bein wet all the time.

-Ah, I get it. Sure, women sometimes get tha, don't they?

- Yep, they do indeed.

-Is tha sexual harassment, talkin 'bout something they get in this book? Like we gotta be careful, ya know, because it's all over social media?

-For fuck sake. Give me patience!

-I am just sayin, as we might already be in trouble with the Doyler guy, don't forget tha.

-Doyler, me arse. He doesn't own every fuckin dialogue between two geezers.

-Jaysus, ye're bein brave today. So, is he back at work yet, cos ya know like, it was only prostate cancer?

-Don't get him started. Be fuckin careful with what ya say 'bout tha. He is pissed at the way some people think prostate cancer is like havin a fuckin head cold.

-I was only pullin his leg.

-Nah, he's not back at work but hopin to start part-time from first of March. Still leakin a good bit and needs to be close to the jacks so he can jump in and have a slash when the urge calls.

-Yeah, can see tha. All the same, it's a fuckin nightmare, this bleedin illness.

-Tha's for sure. Playin havoc with the relationship with his Missus – sure, they can't be intimate. The whole Erectile Dysfunction thing is doin his head in.

-Fuck. Tha's enough to make any man go mad.

-Well, the body is healin well, so tha's a good sign. Now to get his mental state movin at the same rate…

-I see he was out today doin a bit of outdoor work with the Missus. They shifted all their logs in and broke up the crate and cut it up.

-Ah, tha was nice for the two of them, to get out in the fresh air and work together.

-Yeah, grand day, had some giggles. Sure, they both felt the better for it.

-Nothing like laughter to raise ya up out of the darkness.

-True for ya.

-How is she doin anyways? We always hear about him and this feckin illness affects the partner as much as the patient?

-Ah, she is findin it tough the longer it goes on. Like, she's delighted it's all behind them – the operation and all but just the whole incontinence bit and the limp asparagus has her wonderin will they ever be able to be intimate again.

-Yeah. Ya know wha they say? It's sometimes worse for the carer than the one goin through it.

-Exacto. Huge impact on yer relationship and requires major mental strength and strong bond between ya to get thru it.

-I hear he is goin to publish all these dialogues in one book and will add a little more to it when he is done, like he will do some talkin himself in it.

-Yeah, tha's the plan. Just tryin to get a graphic designer on-board to do the illustrations.

-Fuck. Are we goin to be immortalised in a book with images of us and all? I hope the fecker that does the illustrations makes me look good!

-Probably make ya look like a fat bald little fucker!

-Fuck ya.

-Well, are we done?

-I think so.

-Do ya think he'll write much more?

-Probably one or two more dialogues then he'll be done.

-So, we out of a job then?

-Not sure. He has to get the book finished then he may resurrect us.

-Fuck, just had a thought!

-I am nearly afraid to ask... Wha was it?

-Well, between him and the two of us, if he resurrects us, we be like the Holy Trinity. Ha ha ha!

-I knew I shouldn't have asked.

-Say goodbye for now to everyone.

-Goodbye for now to everyone.

-Smart little shite, ain't ya?

-Well, I think so.

-Ok. I am off to sit by the fire and grab a cuppa.

-Me too.

-Til next time then.

-Til then...

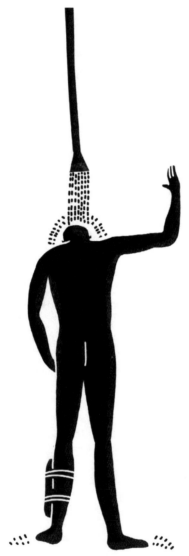

· KARL SMYTH—

CHAPTER 11

Turtle Neck

2 March 2018

-Ya know, when he was showerin the other day, somehow we interrupted his thoughts.

-Now, I'm not so certain we interrupted him. Did he not just think this bit all on his own? Cos I deffo don't want to talk 'bout it.

-Well either way, he's at the keyboards tippin away so I guess he thinks we are goin to do it.

-What if we went on strike?

-How does tha work? Sure, he's in full control.

-Ah Jaysus! Come on, will ya? Say it. Say, I'm not up to this. Ya do it.

-I will start it so.

-Ok.

-So, guys when yous are showering, ye need to be very hygienic down below. Now, carry on.

-Ah, fuck it man. I'm not up to this.

-Go on, I started it.

-Well, when yous are showering, ya need to make certain to clean thoroughly down there – ya know, like around the pecker. Ya need to, ya know, pull the turtle neck back and wash all around, otherwise it gets... ya know, red and sore due to urine seepin out all the time, plus it's lyin in a pad twenty-four, seven.

-Fair play to ya. There now, tha wasn't too bad to say, was it?

-While I'm on a roll, one other thing, can ya tell all yer mates to make certain tha when they're usin the jacks to fuckin aim in the bowl! Nothing worse than havin to go to the jacks when ye're out and ya can't sit down comfortable for all the piss on the seat. Then to really get the back up, yous go and splash the fuckin piss all over the gaff in the cubicle. Now if ye're havin to wear sanitary pants, ye've got to take yer trousers off to change them. How would ya feel when it's bad enough ye're peein in yer pants but now ye've to walk around some other asshole's pee while ya try and change?

-Go on will ya, tha was some rant!

-Well, it has to be said. Fuckin guys think they're playin some sort of video game with their dick when they're in the toilets and leave a mess after them. Wait til they get prostate cancer and we'll see how fuckin smart they think tha all was. Little gobshites.

-I see the Fry has come out.

-Jaysus, he did tha years ago! Sure, the dogs on the street know he's gay.

-Nah, ya eejit! I mean he came out 'bout havin prostate cancer.

-Oh right so, and how is he? Not so QI now, I bet! Did he get to do the season with the letter P in it, I wonder?

-Sure, he knows all 'bout it now, anyways.

-Yeah, this feckin illness knows no boundaries. Doesn't matter how smart or fuckin thick ya are, it will take ya down anyways.

-True for ya, only thing it cares 'bout is tha yer male.

-Nope, ye're wrong there. If ye're a transgender woman who was born with a penis then ya too could get prostate cancer, so it's equally important those women also educate themselves about it.

-Nice one.

-How's he doin otherwise?

-Ah, good and bad. He's down to usin just one pad a day if inside most of the time. Then perhaps two if he is out and 'bout walkin but not walkin too far.

-Dynamite tha is, bleedin deadly all together.

-Yeah, hard to believe he was usin four or five sanitary pants only ten weeks ago and now it's just pads.

-Ah, it's great altogether.

-Besides the use of pads, how's he doin? Like, ya know, in the head like?

-Yeah, gettin there. Sure, hasn't he got us two feckers bleedin chattin away all day every day in his head?

-No bleedin peace there so.

-Ha ha ha! True for ya.

-When is he back to see WALL-E?

-Eh, me thinks in 'bout a week's time.

-Is he gettin his PSA done again before tha visit?

-Yeah, has to get them done every few months now as with such a high reading before the surgery at 19.8 and then a Gleason 9 score and T3. They have to monitor him regularly.

-So, can I ask the big question?

-Which one is tha?

-Has he been given any life expectancy after all this?

-Ah here, for fuck sake. He didn't write this book to scare the shite out of the poor fuckers comin after him who have to go through this journey!

-I know tha but everyone thinks tha way when ya get The Big C.

-To be honest, he doesn't think there is enough statistics to give a good answer as they are only recently catchin this disease in what they consider 'young' patients.

-Fuckin deadly! Bein classified as young at fifty-five!

-Isn't it just?

-So, what's the feckin answer?

-Oh, they reckon he's good for at least another five to fifteen. To be rid of The Big C thereafter is anyone's guess. He also has to be mindful his Da had colon cancer, so tha's hereditary too, but he gets checked for tha every four years. Plus, his Ma died of pancreatic cancer.

-Sure, he could drop dead from something else before then, so tha's grand!

-Yep, his exact thoughts.

-Well, it would be – we are his thoughts.

-I guess we are, just keep forgettin we're not real, like.

-Well, we are real. We are his real fears, thoughts and screwed up thinkin.

-Yeah, guess so.

-Ya know, he's thinkin we're done after this piece.

-Wha d'ya mean done?

-He ain't writin anymore.

-Oh, right so.

-Yeah, he thinks he's done his bit. He says he may come back to it in a year's time, just to update with some final thoughts.

-So, wha happens to us then?

-We go on tormentin the bejaysis out of him, I guess!

-Ah, grand so. Sure, there's lots he could keep writin on his Twitter account. Ya know, like politics and the like.

-Ah, he'd love tha.

-Yeah, bit of a political animal, he is.

-Well, he always likes stirrin the shit, tha's for certain!

-So, we say *Slán* now and sign-off?

-Guess so.

-*Slán.*

-Til next time then.

-Til then...

CHAPTER 12

Paddling

6 April 2018

-What the fuck?

-I know, right!

-But he said...

-Yep, he did indeed.

-And now, this...

-What can I say?

-He's pullin a feckin Arnie on us.

-Yeah – I'll be back...

-I bet Karl, the illustrator, won't be a happy camper.

-I think Karl realises he is dealin with a very dark twisted mind in this guy.

 -So, what's it all 'bout then?

-Sure, does there have to be a reason with this guy?

-Jaysus, tha's true for ya!

-Ah, to give him credit, today is exactly six months since his operation. Sure, he just couldn't let it pass without sayin something.

-Ah yeah, tha's understandable. Big event in his life. I'd say, milestone day for him.

-Indeedo. Although poor fucker thought he'd be fully sorted with regards to incontinence after three months but still fightin a good fight on tha level.

-Yeah, but he is down to one pad a day now, and usin Level Two pads at tha. Sure, he is almost there.

-Try tell him tha. Especially when he has a bad day.

-Ah, I hear ya. Bloody awful. But every morning he places his feet on the bedroom floor, is a day he may never have had if it had not been caught when it was.

-True for ya.

-Funny enough though...

-Jaysus, it's fuckin hilarious! Wha ya like, ya sick bastard with a twisted mind! How can this be feckin funny?

-Ya know yer problem?

-No, but I bet ye're goin to tell me.

-I am, yeah.

-Well, go on then, will ya?

-Ya never let me finish my sentences. Always tryin to be the smart gobshite and jumpin in!

-Go on, will ya! Tell me wha ya want to say then.

-Well, I just wanted to say tha... I don't know now, ya feckin interrupted my flow of thought!

-Well, tha was interestin...

-Ah, go on with ya, would ya!

-Let's get serious for a mo.

-Is tha even possible with us?

-I don't know but he's the one doin the typin, so hopefully it is.

-Yeah, ya kinda forget he is there all the time, typin this away. I even sometimes feel like we are real individuals.

-Now, don't go there again. We have been here before. Many times!

-Yeah, I know.

-Just stick with the sorry fact tha we are voices in his twisted dark head and all will be good.

-Ok. I suppose know our place and our limitations.

-Tha's it.

-So, six months down the track – how is it really for him?

-Ah, deep down he knows he is doin great but just every now and then he gets thrown a curve ball.

-Tha always had me mystified.

-Wha?

-Curve ball. I know there are round ones and then egg-shaped ones tha the rugger guys use but a curved one? Never saw one of them...

-Ah, wha ya like! It's an expression, means ye're blindsided with something tha comes out of the blue.

-Ah, I see... Well, I don't really but go on anyways.

-Well, his curve ball is tha he is doin really well but then, just out of the blue, he can have a bollocks of a day.

-Wha d'ya mean by tha?

-Ya know, he is doin really well with regards to incontinence and then suddenly one day, it's like open season.

-Ah, I get ya now!

-For example, the other day, he had been doin wonderful all week. He even spent time out doin gardenin with her indoors...

-She loves her garden.

-She does, but tha feckin pup she got him...

-I know, like a mud wrestler at times.

-Yeah, but his little face! Ya gotta love him!

-True for ya.

-Jaysus. We did it again, off on our rambles! Wha happened?

-He decided to walk home from work and got feckin soaked.

-Why, was it rainin heavily?

-No, and tha's the issue. It wasn't rainin at all.

-Then, how the feck did he get soaked?

-Figure of speech.

-Wha?

-He leaked all the way home, couldn't control it very well.

-Ah Jaysus! Tha's just the shits.

-Well no, not the shits, more like the piss taken out of him!

-Ha ha ha! Ye're a twisted fucker alright!

-I know but sure, so is he.

-I guess he has to be since we are simply the voices in his head.

-And everything else, how is tha goin?

-Ah, tough at times. Still strugglin with his inner demons.

-I bet.

-The body is healin nicely alright but the mind... Now, tha's another feckin story.

-And his Missus, how is she doin?

-Ah, fightin her own battle. It's bloody hard all round.

-And ya know people think prostate cancer is a piece of piss.

-Well, it is tha – plenty of pieces of piss, if ya get my drift!

-But he knows he is very fortunate to be alive and even with the incontinence, it could be so much worse, so grateful for tha!

-Yeah, I bet he is.

-So, does he feel positive?

-Most of the time. Look, think back on this day six months ago – he was just headin into surgery. Then there was the whole drama of havin to wear the incontinence pants, never mind pads, and at the time, he had to use five a day! He eventually got to a stage where he could use the pads but still, five a day and they were a Level Three pad. And now he is down to one pad a day and Level Two. His goal is to get to one Level One pad a day by beginning of May.

-Only one thing to say...

-What's tha?

-Fair fuckin play to him!

-Ah, ya got it right there for once.

-Some fuckin journey and at the same time, he's writin this so others can learn from it.

-I know. He just hopes tha people will get benefit from it.

-Ah, they will for sure.

-Yeah, I think so too.

-Hopefully, they will drop him a line and check out the Twitter page from time to time.

-Ah, they will, for sure.

-I mean, let's face it, they say there is a book in everyone but this guy has gone the whole mile with not just writin a book but bloody well gettin cancer to write his feckin story.

-Yeah, wouldn't wish The Big C on anyone.

-No, definitely not.

-Ya happy with this lot then?

-I think so, are ye?

-Yeah, I think so and he got to celebrate his six-month anniversary.

-Funny tha ya know, when we are young teenagers, we celebrate these monthly anniversaries over datin our latest mot or boyfriend and now at fifty-five, he is back to doin it for something as serious as this.

-Yeah, I hear ya. But sure, life should be about celebratin every day, as each one is special.

-We will finish on tha so.

-Grand so, let's go get a celebratory pint!

-Til next time then.

-Til then...

CHAPTER 13

Dromance

16 June 2018

-Sssssshhh!!

-Quiet, indoor voice, whisper.

-Got ya.

-He's goin to fuckin kill us, ya know tha, don't ya? He always likes to have the last word.

-Well, hopefully before he realises it, this will be published and he can do nothin 'bout it!

-Sound as a pound.

-Ha ha ha! Should tha not be sound as a Euro now?

-Jaysus, ye're so fuckin full of it.

-See, he went for a walk with his cancer dog today. Mr Buttons, he calls him.

-Yeah, best thing his Missus ever did was convince him to get the pup before he went in for the op.

-Ya know, she reckons they are havin a Dromance.

-A wha?

-Dromance. Ya know, like Bromance but with a dog.

-Even she is turnin into a comedian now!

-Ah sure, poor shites! It's the laughter tha's gettin them both through this. Sure, if ya can't laugh, wha is left, hey?

-Yeah and I hear walkin is good for ya, along with fish ends or fins...

-Come again?

-Walkin is good for ya.

-No, the other shite ya just said – about fish.

-Oh, the fish ends or fins – scientific fact, tha.

-Jaysus, I am nearly afraid to ask but go on, explain it then.

-Well obviously, I don't know the exact facts, but yer man is always sayin tha walkin is good and it helps the fish ends or fins release happy feelings in ya.

-Ye've deffo excelled yerself with tha one.

-Wha d'ya mean?

-It's not ends or fins.

-Then wha is it?

-ENDORPHINS. Ya gobshite! Endorphins. They're a chemical reaction in the body tha releases happy feelings when ya exercise.

-Ah, tha makes more sense.

-Well of course, it does because tha's wha it means.

-So, how is he doin? I mean, just over eight months now. Is he on the dry?

-He's not a bleedin alcoholic, ya know!

-Yeah but is he finished with those bleedin pad things?

-Nope.

-Ah, sweet mother of fuckin Jaysus. Wha?

-Tha's it. Go piss off the Christians now with yer foul mouth.

-Well, it's not like he is one.

-Ya don't have to bring religion into this book, just stick with the facts.

-Hard to do tha with ya as me partner, now isn't it?

-Come on. Let's just stick with the facts. We need to get out of here quick before he realises wha we did.

-Be a bit difficult to 'get out of here' since we are in his feckin head!

-Ok but come on, wha we got to say?

-Well, eight months on and still strugglin but the good news is only one Level One pad per day. Although he had a fuckin nightmare of a week this past one, he had a great day today. Went out with the Missus, daughter and grandson to shopping centre, had a walk around, went for lunch and then drove all the way home again with hardly any leaks.

-Absolutely brillo! So happy for him. But ya know, the urology nurse and doctors did say he would have bad days in amongst the good ones.

-Yeah, he knows tha but as we know, it's so feckin hard to have a bad day now and then. When it does happen, it's almost shattering for him.

-Sure, I mean still not havin full control eight-plus months down the road, is difficult but he is still alive.

-Yeah, he knows tha and gets all tha stuff but it's his fuckin head – it just short fuses now and then with this. It's like ya think ya are just at the end, then some fucker moves the finishing line on ya.

-Little bollocks.

-Tha's a bit harsh. He's doin his best.

-No, the fucker who moves the finishing line!

-Ah right, ya. Fuckin shithead.

-I think he will be alright tho. He has a good support group around him.

-And most of all, tha Missus of his – she's a feckin saint havin to deal with this rollercoaster of a ride.

-Yeah, she is indeedo. One of a kind.

-How is tha goin? Ya know, the matrimonial cognises rights?

-I think ya mean conjugal and they are not rights. Now ya have managed to not only insult all the religious readin this book but every woman in the world.

-Well, there very touchy then, aren't they?

-Just shut it for a bit, let me do the talkin.

-Yeah, ya'd like tha, wouldn't ya? And I say nothing? No feckin way!

-Anyways, there's still nothing happenin in tha department.

-Wha fuckin department?

-The bedroom, ya gobshite. He just isn't feelin it.

-Why? Is she gone cold shoulder on him?

-No, ya eejit. It's him, not her.

-Oh yeah? How many times have we heard tha one!

-It is though, this time.

-Well, I guess with the raising agent gone out of the auld pecker, he's probably all confused. I mean, can't imagine what tha must feel like.

-I'd guess very limp, wet and soft.

-Oh ya bold fucker! I can't believe ya just did tha!

-Ah, he's sound. He knows we are feckin 'bout with him and sure, isn't it the truth?

-Yeah, I guess so.

-Will it ever, ya know, raise the flag again?

-Nope, not by natural means. Didn't we explain tha before, it needs intervention.

-Now, I'm beginnin to feel depressed thinkin 'bout tha...

-I know, very hard to come to terms with, plus only dry orgasms now. No ejaculation.

-Cut down on the purchase of tissues so.

-Always a bright side to everything.

-He really will fuckin kill us now.

-Do ya think he will eventually get fully dry and stop leaking?

-Tha's the plan and everything is indicatin tha will happen. Sure, look at the day he had today.

-Hope so.

-Me too.

-But remember wha they said, it can take twelve to eighteen months for everything to come back workin properly.

-Basically, wha ya are sayin to all those guys out there is stay positive and hang in there?

-Yep, tha's it and best of luck. Hope yer journey is a short one, but don't put pressure on yerself either.

-Well, tha sounds like good advice.

-Yep, we eventually gave some – only took us eight months to do so.

-Ah well, better late than never!

-True for ya.

-Shall we sign off?

-Yeah, think so.

-Ok everyone, we have enjoyed our time with ya. Hope ya got some sound advice from us. If we offended ya with our un-politically correct approach, obscenities and vulgar language, well, fuck ya – sure, we told ya at the start it would be like this. Obviously say tha in the nicest posh voice but seriously, thanks for readin this and may there be many a dry day left in yer life.

-Ah very nice, and well said. Can I just add tha prostate cancer is not like man flu, so when someone gets it treat them with the same sympathy ya would with any other cancer. Don't want to scare anyone but every forty-five minutes a man dies in UK from it. Every year in Ireland, over 3,300 new cases are diagnosed. Let's look after our men and their mental health. Please use the hashtag **#MensHealthMattersToo** and **#ProstateCancer** when tweetin 'bout us. Have a good one.

-Yeah, have a good one, but before we go, one last thought to end on a positive note. Now tha ya have no prostate, ya need never fear rubber gloves and gel! See ya!

-Til next time then.

-Til then...

CHAPTER 14

FOUR TENAS

25 July 2019

-We are the holy trinity. We've just risen from the dead. WE ARE BACK!

-I know, how fuckin cool is this? Can't believe it.

-So, wha's he been up to all this time?

-So fuckin much! This is goin to be a lengthy dialogue, I know tha much!

-Well, let's state the obvious – he's signed a book contract with an indie publishing company.

-Fuckin epic! So, we are goin to be published and famous at last!

-Eh, nope.

-Huh? Wha d'ya mean? Ya said he signed a contract with a publishing company?

-Correcto, but not for this book.

-WHAT!

-Yeah, he is writin another book titled, *Nothing's So Bad That It Couldn't Be Worse.*

-Bastard.

-Steady. The book publishing company felt he needed to tell his story in his own words before releasin this book.

-Right so, but we will get published?

-Tha's still the plan.

-Grand so.

-So, how is he doin? Is he free and dry, runnin around a naturalist colony?

-Nope, still wearin pads twenty-four seven but the majority of the time, they are only Level One and only when he has to go out for long periods does he wear a Level Two pad.

-How is he copin with tha? He did think tha after twelve to eighteen months he'd be pad-free?

-Yeah, difficult some days but most of the time he manages pretty well. Just the odd occasion he has had a few accidents.

-Poor shite.

-How's the bedroom workin out?

-It's not really. He never got round to usin tha pump. He went for a chat with the guy thinkin it be one of the urology nurses but ended up bein a sales rep. Then to add insult to injury, of all things, the dude had eaten cheese and onion crisps for his lunch. Can ya imagine it – sittin in a room talkin about Erectile Dysfunction and havin to smell the breath of cheese and onion? It was as if Mr Tayto was sittin in front of him!

-So, he didn't buy one then?

-Nah, he actually had a little melt down tha day. Came home after the visit and literally couldn't talk for the rest of the entire day. I mean absolutely nowt – not one single word. His Missus knew and just left him to it.

-Wha happened?

-Not really certain... Mr Tayto was talkin about the pump, the different sizes, how to use it and where to buy it. He then asked him would he like to try it.

-Get out the yard, really?

-Yep.

-And wha did he do?

-He politely declined but it triggered something in his head about the sexual child abuse he suffered and impacted him very badly after.

-Poor fuck!

-Yip. Anyways Mr Buttons, his dog even knew he had a bad day and just came and sat beside him all evening.

-Their amazin, those dogs. I hear Vicky got one.

-Yeah, sure it's Mr Buttons brother Vicky got.

-No, ya twat! I mean Vicky Phelan, not Vicky his daughter.

-Ah, the modern-day version of Lady Lavery. She should be on the Euro like yer wan was on the punt.

-Tha's for certain. Wha an amazin woman pushin the boundaries and crumblin the system.

-And here, wha 'bout his mate from the Four Tenas? KleenexMan aka John Wall.

-I am tellin ya he's hangin out with all the cool dudes and we best mention the other two geezers from the Four Tenas.

-Ah, how could we not! PadMan and WeeMan. Fuck, poor WeeMan only had his surgery a few weeks back.

-Do ya think people will get the Tenas link?

-Well, the pads all the guys wear are made by Tena so he came up with a name of The Four Tenas and they've been takin the piss out of John Wall aka KleenexMan tha he was the Robbie Williams of the band goin all solo on them this week in the media over the Medical Card Scandal.

-But fuck sake, the guy is terminally ill.

-Ah, sure they're saying he's just seekin attention. Sure, we are all feckin terminally ill, just the rest of us fuckers walk around as if we are goin to live forever.

-I'm not so sure people will get this humour.

-Who cares? John does and the other two guys do, so they're all tha count.

-I guess so.

-Anyways KleenexMan thinks the same as this dude. He even said as much in a radio interview today.

-By the way, what do they call him?

-PamperMan.

-Ah, no better description for him!

-And guess wha?

-Wha?

-They all have dogs and each of them admit they helped them immensely.

-Here, ya know yer wan got one too? Alfie is his name and has a face tha would launch a ship but big softie nonetheless.

-So, he's hangin out with all the in crowd then?

-Yeah and made some great connections via Twitter, even Gareth O'Callaghan and his partner Paula follow him.

-Sound bloke tha geezer, Gareth. He's talked about mental health issues in men before it was even fashionable to do so.

-Big problem is this whole mental health lark with fellas. They just talk shite most of the time but won't talk about wha they are truly feelin.

-Saves lives ya know.

-Wha does?

-Talkin. Did ya know eight out of ten suicides in Ireland are male?

-Jaysus, tha's fuckin mad and very sad.

-Yep, it truly is but they need to start openin up.

-I hear his Da been done bit of talkin lately and lettin loose about how he feels after his op.

-Did ya hear tha too?

-Well, of course I did. Sure, we are still the voices in his head, so a bit hard not to.

-Yeah, sad as fuck wha's happened. Poor bastard gettin cancer in his kidney and bladder.

-Ya know, he had cancer in his colon twelve years ago too?

-Yep, now this. For fuck sake. No end to it, is there?

-But he had the operation to remove his kidney just over two weeks ago and he is doin great. Up walkin about and all.

-Take more than the Big C to stop tha guy in his tracks!

-How auld is his Da now?

-Eighty-five years young mid-September.

-Incredible.

-Yer man says cancer is like tha fucker who comes for a weekend and then ya can't ever get rid of him – the fucker keeps comin back!

-So then, yer man is gettin to know wha it's been like for his wife all this time, takin on the role of carer and runnin up and down to hospital every day to his da.

-Sure is, and people need to look out for those carers every bit as much as the patient.

-So, gettin back to The Four Tenas – had they similar war stories to share?

-Yep, WeeMan set up a WhatsApp group for them to chat as he only had his operation same time as his Da had his kidney removed.

-And how's tha goin?

-Brilliant. They talk openly 'bout EVERYTHING and it is helpin them all, not just WeeMan.

-They are askin people to follow them on Twitter and then, if they want, they can request to join their WhatsApp Group.

-I hear he's askin Karl to do up a graphic of all four of them in Superpower Hero style.

-Yeah. He reckons tha Batman, Superman and all the other cape crusaders had prostate cancer too.

-Almost afraid to ask, but why?

-Because he says tha the size of their pack in their jocks is deffo the shape and size of an incontinence pad! Ha ha ha!

-Trust tha twisted feckin mind of his to think tha!

-Bet no one after readin tha can now look at a DC movie without lookin at their lunch boxes and wonderin if they've got an incontinence pad under those jocks! Bet its half the reason they wear them on the outside too, for easy access!

-Ah, ye're a gas man, ya know tha?

-So they tell me.

-Ok. I'm off now. Ya comin or wha?

-No, it's just the way I'm standin? Course I'm comin.

-Been a while since he was able to say tha!

-Say wha?

-I'm comin...

-Ah Jaysus. I'm off.

-Ok. Right behind ya.

-Til next time then.

-Til then...

CHAPTER 15

Da

29 October 2019

-Can't believe he's actually goin to write about this cluster fuck?

-I know, totally unexpected. Jaysus, the poor fucker was doin so good too.

-Oh, sweet mother of Jesus! I'm not certain I can write this.

-Hang in there. We'll get thru it.

-Ya better not be pullin my feckin string now, as this could go all tits up on us.

-Yep, well aware of tha.

-So, how was it like? Ya know, findin his Da on the floor like tha, cryin out for help?

-Well, it wasn't exactly a feckin Disney movie scene, was it?

-I know man. I mean wha do we say?

-Well, he found his Da on the floor this afternoon. Poor fuck had been lyin there for five hours, since he tried to get out to have his morning fag.

-He was well shook. Thanks be to Jaysus for the Missus comin over too and managin to get his Da agree to go to hospital!

-Said it before and I'll say it again – some bleedin woman for one woman. True Irish mot. He was blessed the day he met her and made her his bird.

-Feckin only off suckin from her mother's breast when they met, 'bout ten or eleven years auld.

-Here, ya know she was the first girl he ever kissed.

-She better be the last one too or she'll feckin castrate him and I don't mean by medication either!

-But the da? Wha 'bout the poor geezer?

-Ya know, he fought off colon cancer in 2007?

-He sure did, showed tha fucker the door. Bleedin cancer. The reason they created the word motherfucker.

-Well, he managed to get the Da into hospital. Feckin fantastic the nurses in there. They all deserve a medal.

-They can't live off bleedin praise! They just deserve to be paid properly.

-True for ya.

-So, do we know what's wrong with his Da? I mean he was doin so well after they removed his kidney. He was only given tha diagnosis of bladder and kidney cancer in June.

-Ah, bleedin cancer! Isn't it only gone to his hips now. Plus, he had a gut infection and they found cancer on his lungs too…

-Right so, not good then?

-Wha! Yeah right! He's goin to be up doin the marathon next year – no, it's not good!

-Ok, ok! Hold yer feckin horses!

-Yer man doesn't seem to know if he's comin or goin.

-Nah, poor shite is totally screwed up now.

-True what he said earlier – cancer is tha visitor tha comes for a weekend but never fuckin leaves.

-But come here, his auld Da did get a good run at it. I mean he is eighty-five, not like he's in his prime.

-Yeah, but still...

-I know, yeah. It's shite, ain't it?

-Did ya know his Da started smoking when he was only fourteen? I mean, another way to look at it is tha it took seventy-one years to catch up with him!

-Tha's true for ya! And his Da loved his auld fags.

-Here, do ya remember the time he was brought into hospital back in May when they first got him scanned?

-Do I what! Some bleedin man, huh?

-Best bit was they had scanned him, told him he had cancer in the bladder and wanted to do further investigations, so he was placed on a bed in A&E. He gets the longin for a fag because let's face it, when ya are told ya have cancer, ya need an auld fag!

-Do ya recall wha he did?

-Jaysus, he's some man. He gets out of tha bed they placed him on, struts up to the nurses' station where all the docs are gathered around and announces…. 'Excuse me. My two good mates are downstairs lookin for me. Can I pop down to see them?'

-The nurse asks him, 'Who would they be, Mr Poole?'

-Cool as a cucumber he pipes up, 'Benson & Hedges'.

-The nurses broke down laughin.

-Mind ya, the doc wasn't so impressed!

-Always has a joke to make and draws a smile from those around him.

-Indeedo. Some man. Tha's all I can say, some fuckin man.

-Shall we leg it so and get out of here?

-Ah, I guess so. Not much more to say 'bout it right now. I mean, his Da is in the best place to be looked after and sure, he will have those nurses wrapped around his little finger in no time!

-He sure will.

-Anyways, I am goin to the jacks for a slash!

-Til next time then.

-Til then…

CHAPTER 16

End of an Era

25 November 2019

-Sad fuckin day. Bleedin end of an era.

-Tha it is, for sure. The world is goin be a lesser place without him in it.

-I hear he was there til the end with his Da.

-Tha he was. Himself and his eldest daughter, JenPen.

-Standin vigil til the last breath.

-True family til the end. Ya know his daughter had only gotten into the bed 'bout thirty minutes prior and fell asleep as the poor pet was knackered.

-Wonderful support she was too.

-He was holdin his Da's hand all the time. Then he noticed he was takin some very deep breaths, so he leaned in, put his arm around him and whispered in his ear, 'It's ok, Dad, you are tired. It's time to let go and be with Mum but before you do, know that you were the best Dad I could have ever asked for. You were loved by all your family and always will be.' Then three breaths later he was gone, back to Mary, back to the love of his life. Parted in life, united in death.

-Jaysus! Ya have me wellin up here. Now I am a fuckin mess, snots runnin down and all...

-Ah here, it's ok to cry. In fact, better to let it out than keep it in.

-His Ma died from pancreatic cancer, were ya aware of tha?

-Well, I think so. Ya do forget at times tha I am the other voice in his bleedin head, don't ya?

-Ah, I do but sure he'd be lost without us feckin 'bout with his head, never knowin is he truly goin mad or is it just us! Ha ha ha!

-Wha will we do now? Should we just leave it at tha?

-I think so but I think he is goin to put in a wee poem he wrote some hours after his Da died to explain the night and how he felt.

-He likes his bleedin poetry, doesn't he?

-Listen, if Imelda June can start writin poetry, why the fuck can't he?

-May, ya fecker!

-May wha?

-It's Imelda bleedin MAY, not June!

-Oh right, is Bleedin her maiden name so?

-Ah, fuck off with ya!

-Will do. Later then!

-Til next time then.

-Til then...

Goodnight my Father

The deafening sound of silence

The awkwardness of death

Hovering across the sterile floor

Seeking his payment

Patiently waiting, tick-tock

Eighty-five years, he's bided his time

Frequently knocking to no avail

Creeping silently into your room

Like the early morning fog

Forming a white veil upon the bed

No footsteps heard

No sound made

Harvesting the breath of life

As your body lays still

Ever watching, never menacing

As I hold your hand, he lightens your grip

Grasping tighter, I selfishly linger momentarily

The son becomes the parent

The parent the child

Sleep well, you fought hard

She waits for you

It's time to go

No regrets, no anger

You loved and were loved

Goodnight my Father

CHAPTER 17

2 Head Bangers

28 May 2020

-COVID-19.

-Wha?

-Bleedin COVID-19. Can ya imagine it? After everythin the fecker's been thru, now this fuckin pandemic.

-Sure, the whole feckin world is in this one with him.

-Tha they are.

-It's been some journey since he first scribbled our first encounter with him.

-Tha it has, almost four years in total.

-He even went and published his second book first but sure, we'll forgive him for tha. After all, he has now completed this one.

-Typical feckin dyslexic-ASD thing to do! Publish yer second book first and yer first book second. Bleedin deadly he managed to even finish one, never mind two!

-Well, now he also has me almost a year.

-Who the fuck said tha? Was tha yous?

-Jaysus, I thought it was yous!

-No, it was me.

-Who? Wha? Where are ya and who the shit are ya?

-Down here. It's me, Miss Holly.

-Ah no! Please tell me the bleedin dog is not tryin to get in on the act now?

-Ya mean we can talk to animals too?

-Not really, ye're just imaginary but I'm real. He loves me, ya know. As for yous two, yous're just an inconvenience.

-Typical. We get to be able to talk with dogs and we get one with an attitude.

-Cancer brings many benefits, not only do ya get to have voices in yer head but ya also get to be able to understand animals, a real doctor Doolittle!

-Once his cancer dog, Mr Buttons, doesn't try get in on the action, we're good.

-Loves tha fuckin dog he does, loves him.

-Tha he does. Now back to tha book before those two mutts end up takin over this shit.

-So, wha's tha story? Any craic goin on with him?

-He found a lump on his stomach.

-No fuckin way. Is it cancerous?

-Thankfully not. It's a stomach hernia, so goin in for operation.

-Another bleedin male C-section!

-He will start leakin through his stomach with all the holes they are makin when drillin through it. With any luck, there will be none left to leak through his dick, so he won't have to wear pads!

-Still wearin them so?

-Yeah, but only one Level One pad a day and at night.

-How's tha goin for him?

-Ah, he manages but when conducting trainin or givin a talk, he has to be careful how much he drinks beforehand.

-And the morning glory, did it ever return?

-Nope, dead as a door nail, gone for good, or worse in his case.

-I think our job is done here. I mean, we have covered almost four years of this cancer journey.

-The good, bad and ugly.

-Tha's it – life's journey spattered with challenges.

-It truly is.

-I guess we better pack it up or else we will just be ramblin for the sake of it.

-Here, before we go, do they know he gave us our very own Twitter account?

-Jaysus, ye're right! Tha he did! Twitter id is **@2_bangers** and our account name reads '2 Head Bangers'.

-Til next time then.

-Til then…

CHAPTER 18

Bradser

28 August 2020

-He had his surgery for the stomach hernia.

-Said it was a lot worse than he expected, the soreness after, but within a couple of weeks, he was movin better. Just first week was shite.

-His mate Ang was jokin with him the other day about sometimes when women get aulder their tits go east and west, and for men things go south but he reckoned in his case everything below went north!

-I hear he even created a new word.

-Yeah, it's Pagina.

-What the fuck is a Pagina?

-Well, he reckons after the first C-section from the robotic surgery there was shrinkage and now after the second C-section, he says it's like a turtle's neck retreatin into its shell.

-Jaysus, tha's some description.

-So, he calls it a Pagina because it's neither a penis nor a vagina.

-Some nut and he says we're mad!

-I see Bradser's Missus is back on doin Gogglebox. Classy lady. Great comic too.

-Who?

-Ya know her, the one tha looks like the Irish version of Jackie O'.

-Well, her auld fella deffo doesn't look like JFK!

-Tha's for sure, more like a Barry Gibb with the wavey locks and stubble under the nose.

-Here, I see yer man has asked Bradser if he'll ask Jackie O' can she get an Irish comedian to write a foreword or review for the cover.

-Fuck is tha not too sexist?

-Wha the fuck ya on 'bout now?

-Foreword. Isn't tha bedroom talk?

-Ye're as bad as Dunphy callin her a ride!

-Jaysus! He's some balls doin tha if he says it on social media with the Me2 campaign. Bet they're blue too.

-No ya eejit, not Eamon Dunphy, yer wan Maia Dunphy.

-Oh, never knew she was a lesso.

-Oh sweet fuck! We will be rightly sued now, ya know! Anyone else ya want to throw under the bus while ye're at it?

-Anyways, he is simply askin Dee to ask a fellow comedian to write a few words 'bout us.

-Ya mean like the Monsignor guy?

-Who is tha now?

-Ah, ya know him, he's a comedian. Well, at least he thinks he is and been livin here most of his life but still talks with a Yanks accent.

-Jaysus, give me patience! D'ya mean Des Bishop?

-Tha's the fella.

-Well who knows, but hopefully someone will say somethin good 'bout us so this book sells and makes lots of money for the MKF.

-Ya know Ronan won't be too happy with it all.

-Why's tha?

-Sure, he wouldn't even sing *Fairytale of New York* usin the faggot word.

-Ah here, ya can't say tha anymore.

-Well, Shane McGowan does.

-I know but we gotta be careful.

-Ok. Best shut me gob now so!

-So, this is really it?

-Wha is?

-The last dialogue we write in tha book.

-So, is there anything more to say?

-Jaysus, ya know he could write another two books but sure if no one reads this one, no point in rantin on anymore is there?

-Do ya think people will buy it?

-No idea but sure if they don't, he'll just have to write in his journal and leave it at tha!

-Suppose so.

-Well, wha else do we want to say?

-Let's talk a bit 'bout how although we have chatted and bore the bollocks off everyone chattin about prostate cancer, tha it really doesn't matter what type of cancer or if indeed its even fuckin cancer ya have, but whatever it is, illnesses and circumstance in life can fuck up yer head.

-Ya really are tryin to get as many FUCKS in this last chapter as possible, ain't ya?

-Well, if it talks to the lads and they listen, it's worth it!

-I guess so.

-Listen guys, bein a man is not about bein invincible or not showin yer feelings. Be who ya truly want to be and talk to yer mates. Don't let things fester in yer heads.

-Can I say something too? Remember tha no matter how bad things might seem right now, they will improve and ya have to let time pass. We gain maturity, life experiences all with the passin of time.

-True for ya. As yer man is always sayin, his thirty-year-old self thought differently to his forty or fifty-year-old self because ya have more life experience.

-And find mates ya can confide in. Jaysus, even let the voices into yer head at it and let them do the talkin for ya.

-Sound advice, my friend.

-It took ya this long to give me a compliment! And on tha note, I am goin.

-Well then, so am I!

-Safe journey everyone.

-Yeah, safe journey. Now go listen to the Spotify playlist for this book!

-Til next time then.

-Til then...

-Wha next time?

-See ya!

CHAPTER 19

Message from the Author

I have so many thoughts that go through my head at once that I can, at times, find it difficult to get them all down on paper for you. I want to make this a book that you are happy to discover, hopefully find some answers but more importantly, get comfort and solace from reading it. It's a cry from my heart to yours, to let you know that you are not alone with the feelings and emotions that are passing through your thoughts. Also, if at all possible, I hope it will become a comfort for your partner as it will perhaps give them the slightest insight to what is going on.

As a species, we humans are fairly adaptable and resilient. If we weren't, we would never have survived for so long. But it's important to allow yourself moments of sheer self-indulgent pity when it may seem like it's all just too much to cope with. I don't mean you lie in bed for days on end bemoaning to yourself 'why me', but rather have a down day if you feel like it. Don't beat yourself up over it if you do. Sometimes there is no greater comfort than just to lie in bed and let time slip by, especially if you stand up and gravity kicks in with the waterworks!

To your partner I would say, don't always rush with advice, there is a reason we have two ears and one mouth, so listen tentatively. Let your partner blow off steam if required, but also find someone to have a sympathetic ear for you. This illness will impact on your relationship and it's important to be able to talk about that to someone you can trust.

Tips & Tricks

I don't know if I have labelled this section correctly, but I wanted to leave you with some things I found helpful. You may have your own and indeed, others may have shared some with you. These are the ones that I found helpful.

Keep a Journal: Might sound obvious since you are reading mine, but this is actually a very useful thing to do. It doesn't mean you have to publish yours if you don't want to, but I found it very therapeutic to write down my thoughts. It deffo helped with my state of mind and got out any angst that was building up.

Involve Your Partner: You are with your partner because you love them, and they love you! They are going to be taking this journey with you and at times, it might even be harder for them. I always think that in situations like this, it is more difficult for those looking on, as you are experiencing the trauma and in some ways are more in control, even adaptable to the situation. But your loved ones can feel helpless, they may even feel left out or abandoned but that's ok – once you recognise that fact. Unfortunately, you do have to have a certain degree of selfishness with this illness as you have a lot to cope with. You need to concentrate on getting yourself better and being in the right place to cope with this illness.

Be Selfish: I mean this in a positive way and touched on it above. You have to concentrate on getting you better so you can then be of help to others. Now is the time to actually tune out from the world at large and concentrate wholeheartedly on yourself. You need to get your strength back so you can then support those around you. Don't spread yourself thin. Take the time to look after you. Then the time will come when you can look after those around you.

Record & Celebrate Progress: The thing I found most helpful was that at the end of every week I would look back at what had happened and what improvements I could focus on from the previous week. It didn't matter how small the progress was, I celebrated internally within myself. Sure enough, every week I could find something to be happy about. Now, that doesn't mean there were huge improvements or there were no bad days during that week – it simply means I searched for any improvement that would bolster my confidence to prove this journey was moving forward.

Find Your Zone: I am convinced that everyone has a place in their home, or a state of mind they go to for comfort, an activity they do to put themselves at ease and relax. Mine is listening to music, yours might be reading, painting, playing a computer game, watching a movie. It really doesn't matter what it is but find something and somewhere within your home that is your sanctuary. Your go-to place that makes you feel better and take the time to visit that space every day.

Be Patient: I strongly urge you to be patient and yes, I know, there will be times that you just can't or won't. I have been there and still am! However, you are not going to miraculously get better just because you want to – that's not how it works. Patience they say is a virtue, so I suggest you start working on it now. The wonderful thing is there will be progress over time. The only annoying thing is that time has to pass first!

The Lucky One: No matter how hard or difficult it gets, just remember this – you are the lucky one. By that, I mean we are still alive. In 2018, for the first time ever, more men died from prostate cancer in the UK, than women from breast cancer. I know it is not fair and indeed it is not a challenge to see who dies first or has the most deaths – all cancer is horrible, but we are alive. Remember that and celebrate that if nothing else.

Pelvic Floor Exercise Alarm: The infamous Pelvic Floor Muscle exercises! This is something you MUST do three times a day once they have removed the bag from you. The biggest difficulty about doing these exercises is that you will forget to do them! The best advice I can give you is put an alarm on in your mobile phone for the time you are to do them, for me it was 09:00hrs, 13:00hrs and 17:00hrs. By doing this, I never forgot. However, you will have to be patient and always remember everyone is different, so just because you may know of someone who is getting their continence back well in advance of you, don't lose heart. Stick at the exercises and eventually things will come good. My regime was to do ten contractions at each session. Simply contract, hold the muscle tight and count to ten then slowly release and relax. You may find this more comfortable to do while sitting on the toilet but whatever works for you, just go with it.

Employer: How quickly you get your continence back and indeed, the type of work you perform, will dictate how long you are out of work. I would urge any employer who has an employee that had prostate surgery to allow them to visit the office perhaps for an hour or two just to get used to being around people and coping with incontinence before returning properly to work. They most likely may not want to return to work until they have good control and, in some cases, full control back. However, being able to just pop in, meet their colleagues and see how they manage around their work environment could have a significant positive impact on their mental health, as well as their physical recovery.

Self Employed or Company Owner: If you are self-employed or indeed run a company with a number of employees, you will have to take the time to allow yourself to heal and improve. I cannot emphasise enough how important it is that you not only heal your physical body but also, your mental health. You may find that you could be out of action for anything from three to six months. Be prepared for the worst and if things happen sooner, then it is a bonus. Again, similar to recommendations for the Employer section, I would suggest going to the office just to pop in, meet with staff and get used to being in your work environment wearing incontinence pads or pants. There is no glossing over this. It is not nice, and you may feel highly uncomfortable with the entire thing, but just remember you are still alive and this period will pass.

Mental Health: A lot of the focus tends to be on your physical health and incontinence, etc. when you research this illness on the web. However, as you will have hopefully seen by now, having read this book, there is also a big impact on your mental health. No one chooses to be incontinent. It is inflicted upon them and with that in mind, you must try to prepare yourself as best you can. To be honest, it is difficult to prepare for but just be aware that you will suffer with incontinence but more importantly, be aware that it will pass. I found myself getting frustrated and angry at the length of time it was taking to get some control back. Even now writing this almost three years on, I am still wearing a pad. But there has been progress and typically, they say you see this progress really kicking in after week eight, which happened for me. By that, I mean I no longer had to wear the incontinence pants but rather the pads were sufficient for me. Now today, I am down to just wearing one pad per day from five pads! Talking about it to your loved one or a close confidante helps. Don't keep things in, let them out. Remember, if you feel like shouting at the universe, do so – you need to release the pressure valve.

Final Point: All I want to say to you whether you are the patient or carer, I personally wish you every success on this journey. You have my heartfelt best wishes. It is a struggle at times but then again, life tends to be. This illness knows no boundaries insofar as it disregards race, sexual orientation, religion, etc. If you are male (or a woman who was born with a penis) then you have a 1-in-8 chance of getting prostate cancer, but the good news is that the statistics for survival are very strong. Stay positive, stay strong, talk about it, ignore Google and researching too much, just go with the flow and heal at your own pace. But most importantly, allow yourself the odd down day too, you deserve to!

I would love to hear back from people who have read this book, insofar as where they are from, etc. Please feel free to drop me a line at **hello@raymondpoole.com** or follow me on Twitter **@Aladinsane40**